# The Sexually Active Man Past Forty

# The
# Sexually Active Man
# Past Forty

by Stanley Frank

THE MACMILLAN COMPANY

Library of Congress Catalog Card Number: 68-54211

Second Printing 1969

The Macmillan Company
Collier-Macmillan Canada Ltd., Toronto, Ontario

Printed in the United States of America

# Contents

# The Sexually Active Man Past Forty

# 1

# Something Lost in Transition

\* \* \*

WHEN I WAS A YOUNG MAN, A STRENUOUS EXERCISE IN TOTAL recall, radiant weather in New York brought the season for savoring an enduring attraction of urban life. Affable companions interested in contemporary culture always had time for field research on Fifth Avenue looking at the girls in their summer dresses, an equally rewarding project in any American metropolis. Our wives made caustic references to leering, prancing goats, but the appeal of the ladies in full bloom was purely esthetic. That was the party line for domestic consumption, and it even might have been true.

Girl-watching, a flourishing tribal custom since the cave man discovered nubile females on the yonder side of the hill, never has been more gratifying than it is today. Our rising standards of living and sophistication are reflected in the abundance of splendid specimens with lovely profiles from the neck to the knees. Their demeanor never was more provocative, their clothes never more seductive. Every responsive man past forty is aware that women are more alluring than ever, but he seems to have lost something in the transition from youth to middle age.

Although he goes through the motions and the racy patter of the virile male always ready for fun and games, the middle-aged American is nagged by doubts whether sex still holds its former exhilaration for him. Once it was inconceivable that he would be too tired to leap at the prospect of going to bed with his wife, but it is happening now with increasing frequency. He knows that the stories of extramarital affairs told by the office Romeos are wildly exaggerated, but he wonders how they whip up the energy and enthusiasm for even an occasional fling.

The melancholy truth is that he uses fatigue as an excuse for his declining sexual activity more often than he cares to admit. A more oppressive damper on his potency is the feeling that no relief is in sight from the burdens ganging up on him. He resents the incessant financial demands of his family and the strain of competing against bright, young eager beavers who threaten his status. Once he thought maturity would bring some measure of emotional and economic security, but the Struggle is getting tougher all the time. Like an embittered combat soldier long overdue for a furlough, he is convinced that the reward for valor under fire is a standing order to attack an unending series of heavily fortified obstacles.

He is, in short, a typical victim of the mounting social and psychological pressures that are sabotaging the male libido. He also is a member of the most neglected group in modern society. Public and private agencies have analyzed down to the last syndrome the influences of environment on children, adolescents, young adults and elderly people. The attitudes bred by poverty and wealth are examined daily in the newspapers. But the middle-class, middle-aged man is left to his own devices groping for escapes from the blind alleys of a labyrinth.

His wife, in sharp contrast, is the pinup girl of every psychiatrist and sociologist with easy access to a typewriter. During the last quarter-century, more than five hundred books and countless articles have been written on her marital, sexual, social and psychological problems. One stage in her life cycle, the menopause, has been the greatest boon to women's magazines since the introduction of advertising ("Pitfalls of Your Difficult Years"; "New Horizons for Your Mellow Years;" "The Challenge to the Eternal Woman").

Husbands are reminded constantly that wives need sympathetic understanding during the menopause—but the fact that men go through a similar phase, the climacteric, is widely ignored. In the 1930's Dr. Hans Selye, an endocrinologist at McGill University, found that aging exacts the heaviest toll from the male sex glands, a deterioration that begins to speed up after forty. Further research has shown that this biological process often is accompanied by severe emotional disturbances and startling personality changes. Despite such evidence, many doctors still dismiss symptoms of the climacteric as sheer imagination or the querulous bleats of neurotic men.

There are several basic differences in male and female attitudes toward sex. The subtlest, perhaps, are the subjective reactions to the menopause and the climacteric. A woman is conditioned from puberty for inevitable physiological changes after forty. All sources of information now shower her with assurances that the advent of infertility does not detract from her femininity, effectively curbing the "change-of-life depression" that once plagued middle-aged women. Actually, it is a common phenomenon for a woman's libido to rise sharply after the fear of pregnancy has passed.

A man is unprepared psychologically for the impact of age on his sexuality. He knows, of course, that a veteran campaigner does not have intercourse as often as a young recruit. But no one has ever told him that fatigue can induce a premature ejaculation that gives him the mortifying feeling he is as inept as a callow schoolboy. He has never been told that the shattering experience of failing to produce a satisfactory erection is a purely temporary condition and does not foreshadow the grim specter of impotence. Alarmed and uninformed, he does not realize that more insidious forces than advancing age are undermining his sex drive.

"What happens above a man's neck is vastly more important than what happens below his belt," Dr. William Ferber, a prominent urologist in New York, declares. "A man cannot command an erection. It is an intricate process that may be short-circuited by the slightest tension or anxiety. The trouble is that sexual problems tend to become self-perpetuating. The more a man worries about his potency, the more he compounds his psychological difficulties.

"Take a typical situation. A man returns home from a long, hard business trip and, although he's bone-tired, he feels obliged to make love to his wife that night. He probably has a weak orgasm very quickly and fails to sustain his erection until his wife reaches her climax. He is afraid she will think he played around while he was away, so he has another go at it the following night and the result is another fiasco.

"Now he is frantic. Had he waited a night or two until he was well rested, everything would have been perfectly all right. His wife would not have been suspicious of the delay if he had never given her cause to distrust him. Women are much more sensible about such things than men. The chances are he was brooding over an unsatisfactory performance in bed before he went on the trip, and the harder the poor fellow tries to redeem himself the more futile his efforts are. That's how practically all cases of impotence begin. Organic lesions rarely are the cause of impotence. It invariably originates in the mind."

A major difficulty in relieving such fears is that every man who is disturbed by real or imagined complications in his sex life believes his predicament is unique. A woman will describe the clinical details of her hysterectomy at the mention of another female's operation, but a man is so sensitive about his sexual capability he will not tell even a close friend that he is under treatment for a minor prostate ailment. An admission of waning potency is an intolerable blow to his self-esteem. It means he is over the hill—a candidate for the scrap heap.

"It's almost impossible to discuss his declining sex drive with a middle-class man," says Henry Freeman, executive director of the Family and Childrens Service in Pittsburgh.

"You can refer indirectly to his loss of physical vigor and agility, to his jaded appetite for other pleasures, but the moment you approach the area of his sexual activity he freezes up, finds an excuse to leave and that's the last you see of him.

"The situation is easier to handle on other social levels. A working-class man pushing fifty is accustomed to crude jokes about his sexual limitations. He will smile good-naturedly when, after commenting on a well-stacked babe, a young guy in the crowd says, 'G'wan, you couldn't do anything if she gave it to you on a silver platter.' A wealthy man can always find young, attractive women to bolster his ego. More than twenty-five years of experience have taught me, however, that the subject of reduced potency is taboo among middle-class men. It underscores the fear that decreasing virility threatens their earning power and symbols of achievement.

"Another important factor is a complaint that was unheard of a generation ago in marriage counseling. Wives are criticizing their husbands' sexual inadequacy and demanding more gratification in bed. It's astonishing how many women are saying, 'I must take the initiative for all the sex in my house.' They're not getting the strong orgasms described in women's magazines, and they're damned indignant. They feel it's an affront to their femininity. Young women who fancy themselves intellectuals have absolutely no reticence in discussing their sexual techniques and incidence of coitus. They want to show they've read Kinsey and Havelock Ellis, but it also is a sardonic way of knocking down the idea that men are the dominant partners in sexual relations.

"This points up a trend that has not been given sufficient attention. Virility is put to a much more severe test today than it was when women's responses to sex were governed by Victorian attitudes. A lady was not supposed to derive, much less demand, enjoyment from intercourse. It was a chore she tolerated just often enough to appease the animal side of her husband's nature and stop him from running around with loose women. Marital relations might not have been very exciting when wives repulsed amorous advances nine times out of ten, but the refusals gave men the idea they were lusty guys with a greater capacity for sex than women.

"Now, with women discarding their inhibitions, men no longer can coast on their reputations as great lovers. They've got to prove it in bed, and a growing proportion are failing to perform up to expectations. The way things are going, I sometimes wonder whether virility in our society eventually will be measured by the ability to produce a satisfactory erection instead of frequency of intercourse."

Sigmund Freud said, "The most intensive pleasure of which man is capable is the sexual act." It also is a prime source of his inspiration and psychic vitality, but today there are obvious indications that sex is bringing frustration rather than fulfillment to middle-aged men. Authorities who are not in the habit of concocting publicity with alarming pronouncements report a sharp rise in adultery, perversions and traffic with call girls among men between forty and fifty. Couples estranged after more than fifteen years of marriage account for fully 20 percent of the divorces in the United States. The overwhelming majority of the men promptly marry women considerably younger than their former wives.

Such upheavals in established sexual patterns are triggered by psychological conflicts stemming from fear and ignorance. The forties, the decisive decade in the timetable of success, witness the full expression of a man's innate powers—and weaknesses. It is the period of his heaviest emotional and financial loads, and all the self-discipline of maturity must be marshaled to prevent these relentless pressures from warping his sense of values.

Everyone, it seems, descends on him with problems clamoring for attention. His wife, at loose ends with the children finding new interests beyond the home, is more dependent than ever on him for affection and mental stimulation. Older children pose greater problems of education, careers, courtship and marriage. His elderly parents lean on him for emotional and perhaps financial support.

These are a man's proper responsibilities, but who gives him any consideration? Who cares that time is running out on his private dreams? Stiffer competition in business is beginning to tax his physical resources, but who throws him a few kind words to fortify him for the long haul?

Women can cite endless variations on these grievances, but again there is a significant difference that sets the sexes poles apart psychologically. The proposition can be reduced to a salient point: Women do not have to cope with the measurable criteria that confront men throughout their lives.

Comparative yardsticks continually goad a man to strive for more impressive—not necessarily worthier—objectives. There is no absolute definition of success; it is interpreted in terms of the money, prestige or creature comforts other people possess.

The sweetest words a woman can hear are "I love you." It is a declaration made without reservations, a complete acceptance of all her faults and virtues. The reciprocal avowal to a man, "I'm proud of you," is not inspired by his prowess as a lover, thoughtfulness as a husband or devotion as a father. It always is predicated on tangible achievement.

Each generation, convinced it must contend with more difficult problems than the preceding one, shrugs off yesterday's crises as trivial complications. A strong case can be made for the argument, however, that men born during the first quarter of the twentieth century have been subjected to more tensions than any group in modern times. Two great cataclysms, the Depression and World War II, hit them in quick succession. They launched or prepared for careers in a climate of despair during the Depression, then bore the brunt of the sacrifices in World War II.

Now their hard-earned status is jeopardized by drastic trends that are uprooting traditional concepts. The absurd emphasis on youth in America has turned experience, their principal asset, into a liability on the labor market. Seniority, formerly a cushion against competition, now makes a man a more vulnerable target in the frantic jockeying for position on Executive Row. The population shift to the suburbs has created new ground rules for middle-class behavior that contravene old-fashioned notions of decorum, rearing children and having money in the bank to pay bills.

Ironically, the paperback rack in a drugstore carries more books dealing with the cultural influences on primitive tribes' mating habits than a public library offers on the forces affecting modern man's sex drive. For example, millions of boys who saw their fathers' self-confidence crushed by the Depression were saddled with deep-seated doubts of their ability to fulfill the expectations of the masculine role. There is a definite correlation between that reaction and the rising incidence of impotence and homosexuality. Yet psychiatric literature must be ransacked to find even passing references to the Depression.

Since the Kinsey reports were published, innumerable studies of male and female sexual behavior have been made. Some, pertaining to women, are much more informative than Kinsey's work. Too many written by psychiatrists, however, are in a jargon that Dr. Theodor Reik impatiently dismisses as "psychoanese" designed more to impress colleagues with the author's erudition than to enlighten laymen. Sociologists compound the confusion with tedious papers that are as unintelligible as British movies without English subtitles. In 1963, Washington University of St. Louis rendered a notable public service by establishing a special division to translate articles in the social sciences into concise language stripped of technical double-talk.

A more urgent contribution to the clarification of the male's sexual problems still has to be made. The fallacy that his libido operates on a push-button basis is the cause of more anguish in middle age than any other misconception. Most books, particularly those written from the woman's viewpoint, casually assume that the virile type responds automatically to erotic stimulation and always is—or should be—ready for coitus.

The truth of the matter is that the physical and psychological constant in sexual relations is the woman, because her role is essentially passive. As they say in Army directives, all she has to do is furnish the body. She does not have to be aroused and reach an orgasm to accommodate a man. It is infinitely more preferable for both partners, of course, if she is excited in foreplay and brought to a climax, but these conditions are not imperative for her participation in intercourse.

Not so with a man. He must produce an erection, which is far from a spontaneous, invariable reaction when the spirit does not move him, and he must explode in an orgasm to complete the act satisfactorily. He cannot fake the tumescence of his penis or simulate his passion. A wife always knows the intensity of her husband's ardor by the duration and strength of his orgasm. Kinsey constantly qualified his generalizations on men's sexual behavior, admitting that the statistics on their responses were subject to more psychological variables than the data on women.

Most people think of sex as purely a physical function. Life would be far less complicated if it were. A simple illustration of the sharp fluctuations in the male libido is the lift a two-week vacation gives a middle-aged man's potency. While he is away he usually expends more physical energy in traveling and sports activities than he does in the course of his business routine, yet the "rest" is a tonic to his sexual desire, because it is a relief from the mental pressures and aggravations of the daily grind.

Paradoxically, a flurry of potency during a holiday may provoke a man to unreasonable resentment against his wife when he returns to the treadmill. Like a peevish child at the end of a Christmas party, he blames her indifference for the reversion to their previous rate of intercourse. He forgets that he was relaxed and in a pleasant mood on vacation. He does not consider that he was more amorous during foreplay, that the easing of his own tensions made her more responsive to him. All he knows is that he had a feeling of youthful vitality on vacation and now his wife's apathy is stifling it.

This situation and the sequels to it are familiar stories to divorce lawyers and other coroners of marriages killed by ignorance. The husband, convinced that his wife is rejecting him, retaliates by having an affair with a younger woman. The excitement of an illicit liaison and different erotic techniques stimulate his potency, and he decides impulsively to get a divorce, believing he will continue to respond to his new wife with new vigor. His naiveté would be ludicrous if it did not lead to such disastrous mistakes. Within a few months his rate of intercourse has dropped back to its former level, but one marriage has been destroyed, and the second is overcast with guilt and regrets.

Another reprisal leaves uglier scars than a divorce. The husband deliberately abstains from intercourse with his wife to punish her for rejecting him. It is difficult to believe that a man will resort to such a silly, self-defeating trick to vent his rancor, but it is one of the most prevalent causes of marital discord among middle-aged couples. After a while, they communicate in exchanges of barbed gibes that mortify their children and embarrass friends. They share only a hostility that feeds on recriminations long after the original cause of friction has been forgotten.

Some psychiatrists contend that the middle-aged man must learn to accept sexual frustration, because there is no remedy for his declining potency. They maintain that he must lower his sights and submit meekly to reality or he will be crushed and humiliated. This argument is summarized in the opening paragraph of Dr. Edmund Bergler's *The Revolt of the Middle-Aged Man:*

"Man's middle-aged revolt—the sudden discontent with everything (including marriage, professional duties, conventional pleasures) befalling men in their middle age—is the sad story of an emotional *second adolescence,* in which the words are of the cloak-and-dagger variety, the deeds inadequate and the finale a predictable defeat. Inevitably, the revolt is abortive and leads to one of two consequences: acceptance with *good grace,* of the rebel's individual and unchangeable (because self-created) fate—including the wife he will not divorce in spite of grandiose plans—or an even more tangled network of difficulties through which he plunges to find himself exactly where he began, but *full of bitterness and reproaches.*" (Italics Bergler's.)

Nonsense. It is rank defeatism to declare that a man is a helpless victim of despair. It is an antisocial philosophy that does not credit him with sufficient intelligence to make adjustments to physical and psychological changes once he has been told how they affect him.

Above all, the assertion that hopeless resignation is the only solution to a man's anxieties in middle age denies the sustaining power of love. Forget the sardonic jokes; love is not the exclusive province of women. "No one would fall in love unless he had heard about it from someone else," was an axiom of La Rochefoucauld. George Bernard Shaw, who hardly qualified as an authority—his marriage to Charlotte Payne-Townshend was never consummated—said, "Marriage is popular because it combines the maximum of temptation with the maximum of opportunity."

All brides are not beautiful, and few have rich fathers who can provide sons-in-law with free rides on the gravy train. "Marriage begins with a prince kissing an angel. It ends with a baldheaded man looking across the table at a fat woman," Bergler wrote derisively. Very droll—but the devotion of two people who no longer are attractive and still are together after forty or fifty years turns a cynical crack into a touching testimonial to the enduring power of love.

It is no secret that any fairly presentable man whose work brings him into contact with the surplus of women floating around at loose ends today can score regularly in the romantic league if he has the slightest inclination to enter the lists. Why do the majority of married men remain on the sidelines? There are a number of practical considerations that deter a man from kicking over the traces.

The fear of discovery and the furor it will raise at home usually throws cold water on temptation before he yields to it. Furtive rendezvous and hurried intimacies are not much fun for a man who is accustomed to the comforts of the marriage bed. If he has been out of circulation for some time, he feels foolish croaking his old mating calls. Then, an affair is an expensive pastime; a middle-aged Lothario cannot take a girl to a movie and park in a car afterward. The whole thing is not worth the trouble and the consequent guilt feelings. But the overriding reason husbands remain faithful is the abiding love they have for their wives.

Sex is not the quintessence of love, but it is unquestionably the *élan vital* in a happy, harmonious relationship between a man and a woman. The proposition was summed up succinctly by O. Spurgeon English and Gerald H. Pearson in *Emotional Problems of Living:* "When sexual adjustment in a marriage is good it constitutes about ten percent of the positive part, but when the sexual adjustment is bad it constitutes about ninety percent of what is wrong."

During the early stages of marriage the responsibility for establishing sexual rapport falls on the husband, who supposedly brings more experience to the union. He is expected to indoctrinate an inhibited bride in the delights and surging releases of physical love, but the wife's role must change gradually through the years.

A mature woman who does not progress beyond the adolescent level of sexual responses is not a satisfactory mate. She has a responsibility to experiment with more sophisticated techniques of love-making and to cultivate the erotic refinements that excite her husband. Studies of divorce in the United States and England reveal that the failure—or refusal—of wives to make this transition is a major source of conflict between estranged couples.

Dr. A. A. Brill, one of Freud's earliest disciples in the United States, said, "You will always make a mistake if you advise any person about his course in sexual behavior. The only thing you can do is to enlighten and help clarify the problem. . . . The average person does not need advice and the moron or defective will always go wrong regardless of advice. If the patient is of normal mentality, give him enlightenment."

That's what this book is all about.

# 2

# The Numbers Game

***

MEN HAVE ALWAYS EQUATED VIRILITY WITH SEXUAL ACTIVITY—an attitude that is entirely consistent with their biological and social functions. Aggressiveness is the dominant motivation of the male animal throughout nature. He pursues and possesses his mate; the female receives him. Man pits his strength and resourcefulness against the challenges of his environment to make it secure for woman's passive domestic role.

In civilized society, aggressiveness is converted into competition for influence, money or prestige. By the time they reach forty-five, most men have made a realistic appraisal of their capabilities and are reconciled to a subordinate position behind the front runners in the race for the top prizes. But few stop competing sexually with themselves in the numbers game—a contest they cannot possibly win.

Virtually every middle-aged man, regardless of his sexual sophistication, makes the mistake of playing the numbers game at some point. The trap usually is sprung during a period of prolonged stress or fatigue when, after skipping one or two sessions of love-making, he suddenly realizes that his rate of intercourse has been dropping for several years. Goaded by the fear that the reduction marks the onset of impotence, he tries to boost his frequency to the level of his performance in the full flush of youth. It is a lost cause, as futile as trying to stretch his I.Q. by boning up on the *Encyclopaedia Britannica*.

No man is immune from the organic changes that gradually impair all his physical processes, particularly his sex drive, as he grows older. The steady decline of the male's potency after the age of twenty is one of the straightest lines in the statistics on human behavior. It is a consequence of aging that eventually overtakes every man, married or single, a Casanova or a recluse.

Kinsey's survey showed that married men in the United States averaged about one "outlet"—his euphemism for an orgasm—every three days between the ages of twenty and thirty. Thereafter the figures fell in a continuing, downward trend. At forty, the average was less than two a week. At fifty, it was barely one a week. At fifty-five, it dipped below one a week and continued to fade until intercourse ceased at seventy-five for most men with living spouses. Those widowed in the sixties generally had no further sexual experiences unless they married again. Kinsey's statistics conformed with the findings in all reliable studies conducted in this country and England during the last forty years.

Collateral data compiled by Kinsey further underscored the effect of age on the male's sexuality. The capacity to have more than one orgasm a night drops so steadily that most men are unable to reach multiple climaxes regularly after forty. The ability to maintain a full erection for an extended period also decreases sharply. In his early twenties a man can hold his peak of excitement for an hour under continuous erotic arousal, but at forty-five he rarely can last more than twenty minutes before ejaculating.

The aging male's declining sexual activity was a familiar story several thousand years before Kinsey and his associates published their survey in 1948. The scriptures and moral codes of all religions abounded with admonitions against marriages between mates of disparate ages, warning that a husband who was appreciably older than his wife would be unable to gratify her later in the union. Ancient poets lamented the waning of passion with age. Some of the hoariest jokes in

folklore center around the ruses pulled on wealthy old cuck-
olds by ardent young wives and their lovers.

It is significant, however, that the incidence of marital intercourse today is substantially lower than the quotas recommended by the spiritual leaders of three austere religions. The
Jewish Talmud advised a man to cohabit with his wife from
one to seven times a week, depending on the degree of physical exertion in his work, to forestall the temptation of adultery. In the Koran, Mohammed approved of intercourse once
a week with each of the four wives permitted a devout Moslem. Martin Luther was forty-two when he married Katharina
von Bora, a former Catholic nun, and several years later he
declared, "Twice a week does harm neither to her nor to me."
Since it is logical to assume that those pronouncements reflected the minimum rates prevalent among temperate men,
they clearly suggest that the strains of modern living have
made heavy inroads on the male libido.

The crux of the middle-aged man's sexual problem is his
irrational, often desperate, reaction to his diminishing rate of
intercourse. It is absolutely no indication of a corresponding
loss of virility. It does not have the slightest effect on the
emotional intensity of his response to erotic stimulation, but
his psychological identification with high potency does not
permit him to accept a lower score in the numbers game without a struggle. The resolution of the conflict hinges on his
understanding of true masculine values.

The man who recognizes, after brief resistance to the downward trend, that he is going through an entirely normal phase
of the life cycle weathers the crisis, with his enjoyment of sex
enhanced by a new dimension of fulfillment. Maturity refines
tastes to appreciate subtlety in all things. By making finesse,
rather than frequency, the measure of his satisfaction, he sets a
goal he can attain on his own terms. He copulates when he
feels rested or free—if only temporarily—from the tensions
that clamp a brake on his libido.

Now, no longer driven by the compulsion to prove his virility on a fixed schedule, each sexual episode is spontaneous and exciting instead of a routine entry punched on a time clock. Now, too, there is a sublimation of his crude sex drive. Man was not intended to function solely as a procreative machine; there are other, equally meaningful, expressions of his masculinity. Providing the stability that unites the family, establishing a reputation for integrity, tempering strength with gentleness, even devoting attention to national and civic affairs—newspaper readership is highest among men in the forty-to-sixty age group—these are the credentials of the mature male.

The trouble is that many men who do not know what is happening to them physically fly into panics over their imagined loss of virility. The feeling of inadequacy that begins to assail a man in the middle forties who has not made a decisive breakthrough in his career is accentuated today by bewildering changes in business practices that are blighting his prospects faster than he can adjust to them.

Professional skills acquired through long experience suddenly are made obsolescent by technological advances. Automation not only knocks people out of jobs; it eliminates their occupations. Projections of the future employment market constantly warn the middle-aged man that he must move over and make room for a younger generation better equipped to adapt to scientific innovations.

These threats to his status make him acutely sensitive to any telltale of aging, and he does not have to look far. He is confronted by evidence of it every night he goes to bed with the opportunity, but no active desire, for intercourse. Since he associates sexual potency with youthful vigor, he tries to step up his incidence of coitus to assure himself that he is as good a man as he ever was.

He would not dream of attempting to prove it by matching the number of push-ups or laps around the track he could reel off at twenty. Reason tells him he no longer possesses the strength and endurance of his salad days, yet he disregards the physical limitations age imposes on his sexual capability. He expects his potency to erupt like Old Faithful every time he elects to turn it on. When that assumption boomerangs, an insecure man often grabs wildly at straws to prop up his libido.

The sequence of events leading to the emotional crack-up of a forty-six-year-old executive we will call Richard Rowe followed a familiar pattern of the "promotion syndrome," a catchphrase used by industrial medical consultants. Rated off past performances, Rowe was an unlikely victim of the anxieties that impel men to succumb to the numbers game. He had married Laura, a sedate, hometown girl, when he was discharged from the Army in 1945, and her passionate response to him in bed continued to surprise and excite him long after they had settled down to the prosaic routine of a suburban couple with two children. He had never been unfaithful to her.

They knew from the start that it was a good marriage, well worth sacrifices for their future. He went back to college on the G.I. Bill of Rights for a degree in business administration, and things were rough until his job with a shoe company returned dividends on the investment. Progress was slow through the lower echelons of the organization, but Rowe finally climbed within one rung of top management when he was appointed head of the market analysis staff. Although his salary was a modest $12,000, he was content, at the age of forty-one, to consolidate his position pending the retirement of the sales manager—an opening that would pay $20,000 for a starter. He received two $1000 increases, and then his career lost momentum. The raises stopped. Junior executives fresh from graduate schools were pushing him into the background at weekly departmental meetings with fancy theories that impressed the big brass more than Rowe's factual merchandising reports.

Something also was happening to his marriage that neither

he nor Laura could have defined even if they had discussed it. They enjoyed making love as much as ever, but his preoccupation with the maneuvering at the office gradually lengthened the intervals between intercourse until it was usually confined to Saturday nights. Each time, before he dropped off to sleep pressed against Laura's warmth, he resolved they would get back into the old swing. Every Monday, it seemed one of the bright boys pulled a gambit in the departmental meeting that irritated and worried him the rest of the week.

The tensions at the office flared into disputes with Laura over mounting expenses, and his tirades were variations on the same theme. He felt he had been better off when he was earning $10,000 than he was now, with his son a freshman in college and his seventeen-year-old daughter running up clothing bills for parties at the country club he could not afford to join. They had a bitter row when Laura insisted on spending $800 to refurnish the living room. It was so shabby, she told him, that the kids were ashamed to entertain their dates who came from nicer homes.

They did not sleep together for three weeks after the argument. Laura thought he was sulking with injured pride, but actually he was numbed by the fear that he had ruined his chances of succeeding the retiring sales manager with a projection that underestimated badly the market for women's boots in the winter of 1967. He had played it safe by advising against overloading the inventory with a $20 novelty item, but the fad caught on, and by the time the factory could get back into production the season ended and $400,000 worth of reorders had gone down the drain.

When the announcement came in an office memo, Rowe stared at it dully until his cigarette burned down to his fingers. A younger man was chosen for the job. To make his rejection more galling, the company had gone to the textile business for "a dynamic executive with the flexibility to cope with the industry's problems of the technological age." Laura tried to console him that night. For the first time in their marriage, he did not respond to her touch.

The new man's disarming approach threw Rowe off guard in their first meeting. He smiled ruefully and said he was learning how tough it was to anticipate women's brainstorms in shoes. To expedite faster analyses of sales trends, he went on blandly, the company was installing computers to process orders. The operation would be under Rowe's general supervision, of course. Unfortunately, the nine people on his staff would be replaced by two technicians, but his position was secure. Computers were no substitutes for judgment and experience.

The boom was lowered so adroitly that Rowe was back at his desk before he realized he had been reduced to a glorified file clerk for the IBM cards punched out by the machines. He looked in the telephone directory for the address of an executive placement agency, told his secretary he was leaving for the day and held his composure until he reached the elevator.

"You look as though they've been testing a new line of football cleats by running up and down your face," someone said. He turned and saw Helen Breslin, a shoe buyer for a chain of department stores, was in the car. "I'm sorry," he said. "I didn't notice you." He smiled involuntarily. Overlooking Helen, a statuesque brunette in her early thirties who affected flamboyant clothes and mannerisms, was analogous to ignoring a Scottish bagpiper in full regalia.

"There's nothing like the truth to tear down a girl's morale," she said. "I haven't had a compliment since a retarded errand boy made a pass at me at the office party last Christmas. I'll spring for a drink just to hear some lies for a change."

Rowe suddenly decided he was in no mood for an interview at a placement agency—or to see the despair on Laura's face when he told her about the computers. Maybe Helen, who knew all the gossip in the trade, could tip him off to an opening somewhere. By the third drink he had told her more than he intended, and she was feeding his self-pity by commiserating with him on the raw deal he had been given.

She looked at him over the rim of her glass. "The next thing you know, computers will be telling people when to go to bed together."

He remembered that she had gone to Reno for a divorce the previous year. "I'm the old-fashioned type," he said, wondering how far he could or wanted to go. "I still use the abacus."

"I've never had an abacus," she said. "Isn't that a thing with a lot of balls? Sounds like fun."

They went to her apartment, and an hour later he called Laura on the phone beside the bed and told her curtly that he had to finish a survey that would keep him in town overnight, then turned back to Helen's voluptuous body. The next morning she brought him to a climax again.

He felt hollow with guilt when he reached the office, but it faded as he visualized Helen lying next to him. Three orgasms in fourteen hours. More than he had had with Laura in a month. The excuses men invent to assuage their conscience began to turn his guilt into resentment of Laura. It was not entirely his fault that he had been unfaithful. Laura's indifference had been cheating him for years of the stimulation he needed. No wonder he had lost his promotion. Laura might be willing to stagnate in middle-aged apathy, but he refused to accept it. He took Helen to lunch at a chichi restaurant where she held court regularly and reveled in the thought that she had chosen to go to bed with him instead of the charm boys, ten and fifteen years younger, who swarmed around her. That night he told Laura he would have to inspect a new system of inventory control at the company's plant in St. Louis over the weekend. He spent it in Helen's apartment.

Rowe had seen enough examples to recognize that he was acting like a middle-aged fool who had suddenly rediscovered sex, but he told himself that his affair with Helen was different from the usual philandering for new thrills. Sleeping with a young, full-blooded woman and gratifying her was incidental to the feeling of vitality she gave him—the assurance that he could still compete in the mainstream of life against younger men. His nights in town and trumped-up weekends in St. Louis became more frequent. Like a compulsive gambler pressing his luck, Rowe was obsessed with riding the peak of his potency before time ran out on him. It was sustained for two months by the excitement of an illicit bed and the novelty of Helen's amorous techniques. And then he received the quarterly bill for his son's college tuition. He would have to borrow it; the money he had been spending on Helen had stripped his bank account.

He was impotent with Helen that night and failed again to produce an erection the next morning. When he left, they understood tacitly that it was the end of the affair. Laura accepted his return impassively. She was too drained emotionally to ask questions, and he was too ashamed to offer explanations. To outward appearances the marriage was intact, but he knew their relationship would never be the same again.

There is no clue to the male's psychology more revealing than the sharp contrast between his frantic efforts to force his slackening sex drive into high gear and his sensible adjustment to other physical changes in middle age. He stops trying to impress anyone with his muscles or his business acumen after two martinis at lunch. He watches his weight, makes at least one stab at cutting down on smoking, passes up social engagements the night before a big day at the office, abandons delusions of grandeur in weekend sports activities and waits for the light to change before crossing the street in heavy traffic.

He even makes wry jokes about his infirmities: "Long hours don't bother me. I'm fresh as a daisy after a blood transfusion. . . . They're not making mirrors the way they used to when I was a boy. They all come with built-in wrinkles nowadays. . . . If they keep on reducing the type in menus, I'll have to learn

Braille or starve to death. . . . I think I'll skip this round. I'm allergic to ice."

Physical deterioration actually begins much earlier than most people suspect. The eye, a marvelously intricate organ, starts to lose its acuity at the age of eight, and the decline is so steady thereafter that 95 percent of men and women need glasses in their middle forties. The ear's ability to register high-pitched sounds already is fading at the age of ten. By adolescence there is an increasing preference for highly seasoned foods to stimulate tired taste buds. The peak of muscular strength is attained at twenty-five and is held so briefly that five years later the loss of speed and stamina is obvious even in professional athletes who keep in topflight condition.

The organs affected most drastically by aging, however, are the male sex glands. There is a distinct drop after forty in the hormones produced by the endocrine glands, particularly the secretions of the testicles, and the muscles involved in ejaculation become flabby. Although these biological changes reduce the rate of coitus, the process is so gradual that it is imperceptible from one year to the next under normal conditions.

There's the rub. "Normal conditions" in modern, urban society are almost as unknown as a pressure-free vacuum is in nature. Every man caught up in a competitive situation is subjected to abnormal tensions that intensify the impact of age on his sexuality. Since Dr. Hans Selye's pilot studies in Montreal thirty years ago, countless clinical tests have shown that the sex glands shrink and become less active in inverse proportion to the strains on the nervous system. As Dr. Selye explained in *The Stress of Life,* "At times of imminent danger, in the face of extreme stress, the body must use all of its reserves just to keep alive; while it does this the less pressing demands of reproduction are necessarily neglected."

Achievement and potency are associated so closely in a middle-aged man's psychological frame of reference that an imagined deficiency in either sphere touches off a vicious circle of apprehension. Financial worries or threatened down-grading in status reduce his sexual activity, which in turn causes him to suspect that he is something less than a virile fellow able to bear up under the competitive gaff.

Unfortunately, most men disturbed by fears of sexual in-adequacy are reluctant to seek professional help until their doubts take root in serious neuroses. A common, entirely groundless, concern is the size of the penis. *Sexology* magazine recently made a breakdown of the questions asked most fre-quently by readers during the last ten years. Inquiries relating to underdeveloped genitalia were third on the list after impo-tence and premature ejaculations.

Anxieties pertaining to a subnormal penis generally are a carry-over from boyhood, when there is a good deal of covert peeking and cross-checking in locker rooms. After a swim, for example, a youngster whose genitals have been shrunk by the cold water may be overcome by a feeling of inferiority upon comparing his "equipment" with that of an older boy who has not been in the water yet. The sight of a naked adult may have the same effect on a frail, diffident boy whose lack of interest in sports and strenuous hobbies sets him apart from his age group. Such incidents can lead to a divorce or a psychiatrist's couch thirty years later.

All myths to the contrary, an adult with a penis too small for satisfactory copulation is a medical rarity. An erection of only two inches is sufficient for intromission in the vagina and bringing a woman to an orgasm. In a flaccid state, the penis is about four inches long, and full erections range from five to nine inches.

Further—and this point cannot be emphasized too strongly —the dimensions of the penis are a negligible factor in grati-fying a woman. The consensus of articulate women is that the supreme pleasure of the sexual act is the sense of fulfillment in receiving a lover and surging with him to a climax. There is no definitive feeling of the length or girth of the penis. It is, rather, an all-pervasive sensation that transcends a few notches on a ruler.

A prime source of distorted notions about sex is, paradoxically, the Kinsey report—the most comprehensive statistical study ever made. Physicians and marriage counselors have found that preoccupation with the numbers game, the basic complication of most middle-aged men with sexual problems, can be traced to the wide publicity given Kinsey's average rates of intercourse on various social levels. Few laymen labored through the 804 tedious pages and interminable tables of Kinsey's survey. Their misconceptions were gleaned from excerpts in newspapers and magazines that focused attention on frequency of "outlets."

The flaw in Kinsey's material was that he neglected the element of love as the vital spark of a healthy and durable sexual relationship between a man and a woman. He answered that criticism by declaring that it was "impossible to measure love" and that it was not the function of a scientist "to turn philosopher, poet and moralist."

Kinsey defended his statistical interpretation of sex on the grounds that it would "help in the understanding of particular individuals by showing their relation to the remainder of the group." Yet he repeatedly qualified his conclusions by admitting that psychological intangibles made the differences in potency among men greater than the variations in all other mental and physical attributes. He found a differential of forty-five thousand to one between the extremes in the twelve thousand subjects who were interviewed for the survey. The low man, apparently in good health, was reported to have ejaculated only once in thirty years, while the star sexual athlete, described as "a scholarly and skillful lawyer," claimed he had been averaging more than thirty orgasms a week for thirty years. Since Kinsey gave no details, it must be assumed that the overwhelming majority of the orgasms were induced by masturbation. A successful lawyer hardly would have time for the amenities of heterosexual copulation thirty times a week, even with a harem in residence.

The huge sale of the Kinsey report was cited by Geoffrey Gorer, an English anthropologist, as a flagrant example of "the popular and widespread American habit of rating oneself." Gorer declared that Americans are so insecure they need the "justification by numbers" to engage in sex without feelings of guilt.

That same year (1948) Dr. Oswald Schwarz, an eminent Austrian urologist and psychologist who specialized in male sexual disorders, was completing *The Psychology of Sex*. Dr. Schwarz, whose professional experience was confined to Europe, wrote:

"Man is obsessed with a tendency to valuation; we cannot accept differences between things just as facts, but instantly attribute to them values, that is to say, we take them as indications of superiority or inferiority. Whether this is an innate trait of mankind or the effect of a basically commercial way of thinking or the manifestation of a 'universal inferiority complex' may be left undecided. Nowhere is this tendency more harmful than in matters of human intercourse, and particularly in the relationship of the sexes."

The American male past forty who is struggling to keep up with competition often is stampeded into pursuing false values to demonstrate his fitness for remaining in the race. "It is everyone's ambition, man's as well as woman's, to stay young or—to put it more correctly—'youthful,' " Dr. Harry Benjamin observes. "To the woman this means, first of all, her appearance. To the man it means, above all, sexual potency."

A middle-aged woman who affects the clothes and mannerisms of a giddy girl is ludicrous, of course, but she hurts no one and is happy in her self-delusion. A man who tries to turn back the calendar with sex courts disaster, for his shortcuts invariably are self-destructive.

# 3

# The Denial of Reality

✹✹✹

A MAN'S SEXUAL PROFILE IS LIKE A THUMBNAIL BIOGRAPHY
compiled from sketchy newspaper clippings. His known experiences, achievements and emotional reactions are not always
a reliable index to the influences that have motivated him and
molded his personality. A sexually maladjusted man may succeed in covering up a deep-seated fixation behind a smoke
screen of two-fisted virility until he reaches middle age. Eventually, though, the subconscious drives that are plaguing him
break through his defenses and effect drastic changes in his
pattern of sexual behavior.

Sexual deviations seem to spring up suddenly in mature
men who have never been suspected of such tendencies, but
there always is advance warning of these impending conflicts.
The trouble is that the danger signals are ignored or arbitrarily
condemned as moral offenses.

Most people, if asked to define deviant behavior, mention
homosexuality and two or three erotic perversions. They do
not realize that a man is going through an emotional and
sexual crisis when he abruptly curtails intercourse with his
wife for no apparent reason or tries to go to bed with every
available female in sight, when he begins to drink heavily to
prime his libido or immerses himself in work and withdraws
from sex. Any marked variation in a middle-aged man's sexual
conduct may be symptomatic of a serious disturbance, for virtually all aberrations stem from the same neurosis—the
Oedipus complex.

Dr. Ernest Jones, Freud's biographer, said Freud's greatest discovery was the universality of the Oedipus complex. Freud himself ruefully observed that it was the major cause of the public's antagonism to psychoanalysis. Opposition was even more violent in professional circles for more than a quarter of a century after he wrote, "There is no possible doubt that one of the most important sources of the sense of guilt which so often torments neurotic people is to be found in the Oedipus complex."

In his lectures, Freud repeatedly told of an incident during World War I that illustrated his colleagues' antipathy. One of his disciples was assigned to duty on the Russian front with the German Army medical corps and was so successful in treating cases of hysteria and battle fatigue that he was asked to explain his methods in a series of nightly seminars held in field hospitals.

"For a time all went well," Freud said, "but when he had introduced his audience to the Oedipus complex, a superior officer rose and announced that he did not believe this, it was the behavior of a cad for the lecturer to relate such things to brave men, fathers of families, who were fighting for their country, and he forbade the continuation of the lectures."

At that point Freud always paused, looked at the audience and asked quizzically, "And what is this terrible Oedipus complex?"

The term was derived from *Oedipus the King,* the play by Sophocles that is generally regarded as the masterpiece of Greek tragedy. According to the legend he dramatized, Apollo told Laius and Jocasta, the king and queen of Thebes, that they were to have a son who would kill his father and marry his mother. When Jocasta delivered a son, Laius, fearful of the prophecy, drove a metal pin through the infant's ankles and ordered a shepherd to let him die of exposure on a nearby mountain. The servant took pity on the baby and gave him to a messenger from Corinth. The infant was presented to the childless king and queen of Corinth, Polybus and Merope, and was raised as their heir. The baby, who had been disfigured by the pin, was named Oedipus, which meant "swollen feet."

Oedipus grew to young manhood unaware of his origin until a drunken reveler at a banquet told him he was not the real son of Polybus. Disturbed by similar rumors, Oedipus went to Delphi and asked the oracle who his parents were. The oracle evaded the direct question, but warned him that he would kill his father and marry his mother. Believing the prediction referred to Polybus and Merope, Oedipus left Corinth to escape his dreadful fate.

While wandering in search of a new home, Oedipus fell into an argument with an old man who ordered him to make way for his chariot at a crossroads. The hot-tempered Oedipus refused and in the ensuing fight killed the stranger and all his attendants except one, who fled to Thebes with news of the murder. The slain old man was Laius. The first half of the prophecy was fulfilled.

Continuing his journey, Oedipus reached Thebes in the midst of a crisis. The Sphinx, a winged monster that was part lion and part woman, was killing the young men of Thebes and refused to leave until its riddle was answered. The throne of the kingdom and marriage to Jocasta, the widowed queen, were offered as rewards for solving the riddle: "There is a creature two-footed, and also four-footed, and three-footed. It has one voice. When it goes on most feet, then it goes most slowly." Oedipus answered that the creature was man, who crawls on all fours as a child, walks on two feet as an adult, then hobbles with a cane in old age. The Sphinx then killed herself, and Oedipus assumed the throne and married Jocasta, who bore him four children. The prophecy had come full circle.

Thebes prospered under Oedipus until it was struck by a terrible plague. Oedipus sent Creon, Jocasta's brother, to Delphi to ask the oracle how the city could be saved. Creon reported that the plague would be lifted when the murderer of

Laius, who was living in the city, was executed or banished. Pressing an investigation of the murder, Oedipus learned that a witness had said it was committed by a band of thieves at a crossroads. Remembering his slaying of an old man at a crossroads, Oedipus revealed the oracle's prophecy concerning him. While Jocasta, in mounting terror, tried to assure Oedipus the oracle was not to be trusted, a messenger arrived from Corinth with news of the death of Polybus. Since Oedipus had not murdered Polybus, his father, Jocasta argued that the prophecy obviously was false. Under cross-examination, however, the messenger admitted that a shepherd had given him a newborn infant with pierced ankles who was brought up as Polybus's son.

Oedipus's maimed feet were the clue to his true identity. Jocasta, realizing she was guilty of incest with Oedipus, hanged herself. Oedipus, in a paroxysm of self-revulsion, tore out his eyes and sentenced himself to banishment for having committed the heinous crimes of parricide and incest— offenses that condemned him to eternal damnation.

Freud was denounced for interpreting the legend as symbolic of the sense of guilt everyone feels for having had an early incestuous attachment for the parent of the opposite sex and hostility toward the other parent. He further outraged Victorian morality by asserting that sexual awareness begins in infants as early as six months.

The abuse that was heaped on Freud for expressing such repugnant ideas elicited a wry comment from him: "It seems to be my fate to discover only the obvious; that children have sexual feelings, which every nursemaid knows." The reference puzzled people who did not come from a middle-European background, but it was a common practice among German nursemaids to soothe an irritable male infant by stroking his penis and testicles.

The controversies over Freud's theories obscured the monumental contributions he made as the first scientist to trace human behavior to its origins in early childhood. John Milton said, "The childhood shows the man as morning shows the day." Later, an aphorism, "Give me the first seven years of a child's life and I care not who has the rest," was quoted so widely that it was attributed not only to a Jesuit priest, but also to Jean Rousseau, Karl Marx and Friedrich Froebel, the founder of the kindergarten system. Yet no one had ever explored the field of child psychology until Freud studied the aftereffects of early experiences and impressions on his patients.

Freud's work with adults convinced him that an individual's basic qualities of character are established by the age of three and that those traits—especially attitudes toward sex—may be modified but are not altered significantly by later events. He studied hypnotism under Jean Martin Charcot, a famous French neurologist, to probe into the subconscious and uncover forgotten childhood incidents—or guilty memories. When hypnotism proved unsatisfactory for that purpose, Freud evolved his method of psychoanalysis to unlock the secrets that were haunting his patients.

The Pandora's box opened by Freud was so shocking that some professional journals refused to publish his early papers. He reported an "inexhaustible" capacity for masturbation in adolescent boys, a high incidence of latent homosexuality among married couples and a wide range of perversions practiced by upper-class men and women. Nothing was as abhorrent, though, as his assertion that all infants have incestuous feelings for their parents.

It is entirely understandable why the Oedipus complex (called the Electra complex in a daughter-father relationship) was a revolting concept to the public. Incest is the most unspeakable of all sexual offenses. It is one of the two universal taboos—molesting children is the other ban—that has been enforced in all primitive and civilized cultures. Even where incest was sanctioned in ancient Egypt, Peru and Hawaii to protect the purity of the royal bloodlines, marriages between brothers and sisters were uncommon and always were viewed with deep misgivings.

In passing, it is ironic to note that the last remaining semblance of incest is found in the endogamous marriages—or unions confined to a small social group—of European aristocracy. Virtually all the reigning and deposed royalty of Western Europe is descended from Queen Victoria of England. In sharp contrast, many North American Indian tribes went to such lengths to avoid incest that, despite their sparse populations, they did not permit third cousins to marry, because there was a danger that a closer blood relationship might have been overlooked somewhere along the line.

The incest taboo is a perfect example of the practical social considerations that dictate all controls on sexual conduct. In prehistoric times the race obviously was propagated for many generations by intercourse between siblings, mothers and sons, fathers and daughters. Each family was a self-contained social unit; other groups were potential enemies, and taking mates from them brought dangerous reprisals. Further, the number of offspring a family produced was its best guarantee of survival. Proximity and the natural affection of parents for children undoubtedly led to sexual relations within the family. The life span was very short, and when a mate died it was safer, and more convenient, to cohabit with another member of the family than it was to take a stranger for a partner.

Primitive man had no knowledge of genetics, of course, and was unaware of the biological dangers of close inbreeding. Yet very early in his social evolution he recognized the necessity for banning incest. Why? To eliminate the conflicts that disrupted the family and weakened its united defense against enemies. A father and a son competing for the sexual favors of the wife-mother inevitably caused discord and violence. Conversely, a jealous mother and daughter bidding for the amorous attention of the husband-father resulted in intolerable tensions.

Stone Age man must have learned through experience that intimate sexual contacts within the family led to a confusion of attitudes that was inimical to the authority of parents. After a father had intercourse with a daughter, for example, he could not command the obedience and respect that were essential for maintaining his control of the group and passing on the traditions that were the fabric of its social structure.

Despite all the moral and legal interdictions against incest that have been in force for countless millenniums, it has not been eradicated completely in modern society. Veteran policemen know it is a cause of crimes of violence that erupt inexplicably in quiet, apparently respectable families on all social levels. Everyone has read newspaper stories about parents and children suddenly going berserk and assaulting other members of the family. The stories often are hushed up after the first blaring headlines, because interrogation reveals that the assailant's discovery of an incestuous relationship within the family triggered the attack. Newspapers make guarded references to "unnatural acts" in accounts of arrests for rape, homosexuality and indecent conduct, but there never is an allusion to incest. It is too offensive for even the vaguest insinuation.

Freud's diagnosis of the Oedipus complex was distorted by critics who regarded any discussion of sex as pornography. "Freud wanted to convey, simply, that between the little boy and his father there is a natural rivalry which shows itself unconsciously even after the boy has become adjusted to his father," Dr. A. A. Brill, Freud's first American translator, remarked. More importantly, Freud wanted to warn overprotective mothers that inordinate attention lavished on young sons fostered incestuous feelings that resulted in sexual maladjustments later in life.

Soon after he established his private practice in Vienna, Freud was startled to discover that many men who went to him for treatment of impotence, homosexuality and other disorders had slept regularly with their mothers until they were thirteen or fourteen years old. Some confirmed bachelors habitually crept into bed with their mothers whenever they did not feel well. Brill reported the case of a forty-year-old man who had shared a bed with his mother until she died.

Medical literature is replete with weird case histories of men with pathologically jealous mothers. Women have threatened to castrate their sons to stop them from marrying. Middle-aged widows and divorcees blandly tell physicians they are unable to fall asleep without the "security" of their mature sons' bodies pressed against them.

In 1965, a study of four hundred adolescent male narcotic addicts from lower-class families in New York revealed that many mothers sabotaged efforts to cure the boys, because they wanted to make their sons dependent on them for money to support the habit. "The mothers marry men who are generally passive or abandoning," the report stated. "Due to their own inadequacies as women, they replace marriage with mother-hood." Investigators found that some women flushed their sons' withdrawal medication down the toilet. Others encouraged the boys to pawn household articles or gave them $5 for "haircuts" several times a week to buy dope.

Unlike Philip Wylie's diatribe against Momism a half-century later, Freud was the voice of reason in explaining the psychological relationship between mothers and male infants. He patiently pointed out that it is entirely natural for the baby to prefer the mother to the father. The mother attends to all the baby's needs; she feeds him, comforts him when he cries, plays with him and coddles him to her soft, warm breast. The father is an intruder in the baby's sheltered world. He is a big, rough stranger who seizes him from his mother's familiar embrace and makes loud, terrifying noises.

Fear of the father turns to resentment when the child begins to notice that he deprives him of his mother's attention. She kisses the father when he arrives home and stops playing games or answering the child's interminable questions. She

sleeps with the father behind a closed door in the big, luxuri-
ous bed where the child once was welcome. The father represents the threat of dire punishment the mother is too indulgent
to administer. It hardly is surprising that the female's appearance and mannerisms are more attractive than the male's to a
young child.

Up to this point, Freud's exposition of the Oedipus complex
was as inoffensive as a primer in domestic science for high-
school girls. There was a furious uproar, though, when he went
on to assert that a little boy discovers his penis as a source of
gratifying sensation between the ages of six months and three
years. Sexual reactions are not aroused in a girl at this early
stage, because the clitoris, the female organ homologous to the
penis, is not exposed and consequently is not stimulated when
she is bathed, dressed and fondled.

The boy touches his genitals to induce a pleasant feeling
and promptly learns that grownups disapprove of his behavior. His hand is slapped, and he is reprimanded. When he
persists, he is punished more severely and may be told that his
penis will fall off if he continues to play with it. The boy does
not believe the threat but presently he sees his mother, a sister
or a girl playmate undressed and notices that the part of the
body he values so highly is missing.

According to Freud, the "mutilated" female genital area
comes as a profound shock to the boy. Now he is terrified by
the threat of castration, for he has seen what he assumes to be
evidence of what can happen to him. "Depreciation of
women, and aversion from them, even horror of them, are generally derived from the early discovery that women have no
penis," Freud said. "If the idea becomes a fixation," he added,
"it resists all the influences of later life and makes the man
incapable of dispensing with a penis in his sexual object, so
that such a person . . . must become homosexual, seeking his
sexual object in men who through other physical and mental
qualities remind him of women. Real women, as they become

known to him later, are excluded from being sexual objects to him because they lack the essential physical attraction."

At this critical juncture, the father supersedes the mother as the dominant influence in the boy's emotional development. If the father gives the boy affection and shares an interest in the activities and impressions that engage his restless attention, the child makes a positive transition into a masculine-oriented world.

"The Oedipus complex thus vanishes and the rivalry between father and son no longer has reason for existing," Brill wrote. "The little boy then makes peace with the father. Having always admired him and considered him omnipotent and omniscient, he now adjusts himself to the father by identifying himself with him. The identification is a sort of 'assimilation,' or an introjection of the father into himself.

"All the fears, prohibitions or commands which hitherto came from the father are now incorporated into the boy's mind . . . and constitute what we call one's conscience or super-ego. It is as if the little boy thought, 'I am now as big and strong as father, or even bigger and stronger than he.' It is this standard of measurement which is responsible for all our progress. Every normal boy always tries to outdo his father; sons who just obey never amount to much. Progress consists of not following in your father's footsteps. History shows that this is true."

There are more schools and splinter groups in psychotherapy than shades of political opinion in France, but all subscribe to Freud's interpretation of the Oedipus complex. They agree unanimously that the period between the ages of four and six is decisive in shaping the sexual attitudes of the child when he reaches maturity.

"The degree to which a man can get through any crisis in virility depends largely on his identification with his father," says Dr. Marie Nyswander, a prominent psychiatrist in New York. "In every case I have ever treated or studied involving a male sexual problem, the patient invariably had been unable to establish rapport with his father early in childhood. The father was not around or he was preoccupied with work. If the father was available, he was indifferent to the boy or impatient with him or alienated him by making him conform to a too-rigid code of behavior.

"It is significant that most men with sexual difficulties never played rough-and-tumble games when they were kids. They were under the thumb of domineering mothers who flew into tantrums if they came home with dirty faces and mussed clothes. Their fathers were so henpecked themselves that they were afraid to say, 'Stop making a damned sissy out of the boy. It will do him good to get knocked around a little and learn how to compete against kids his own age.'

"The Oedipal conflict is resolved only when a boy establishes identification with his father. It is his biological, historical and psychological link with the unique qualities of virile men—courage, curiosity and adventurousness. It is the motivating force that makes him want to read about Caesar, Napoleon, explorers and great athletes. It is the essential factor in his background that enables him to cope with the doubts and disappointments which confront him in middle age. A man who is sure of his virility has no need to prove it by accumulating money, self-serving titles or sexual conquests."

One of the commonest, and least understood, manifestations of the Oedipus complex is the obsession with work that suddenly grips men past forty. The phenomenon is not confined to this particular age group, of course, but younger men are driven by different compulsions. When a middle-aged man abruptly pushes aside all other interests and immerses himself in work, it usually is a panicky reaction to his declining rate of intercourse and imagined loss of virility.

He tries to reaffirm his masculinity—to himself, at least—by channeling his energy into a socially acceptable sublimation of his sex drive. He manufactures work by fussing over details, attending to tasks that should be delegated to subordinates, turning simple chores into elaborate projects. It pleases him to be known as the office troubleshooter and the worrywart of the family.

"Only a rugged man can carry such a heavy load of work and responsibility," he rationalizes subconsciously. "Pop would be proud of me if he saw how conscientious I am."

The man who withdraws from sexual activity appears to be the antithesis of the middle-aged Don Juan who chases women indiscriminately, but both are assailed by doubts of their prowess as males. Both have been crippled emotionally by the Oedipus complex, which makes it impossible for them to sustain a normal relationship with one woman.

Of all the prototypes drawn from fiction, none has been the subject of more exaggeration than Don Juan, a character introduced in Spanish drama in the seventeenth century. He is pictured as a blithe seducer, a great lover so infatuated with women that he cannot resist their allure.

The exact opposite is true. The Don Juan is an inferior lover and, worse yet, a woman-hater. He stalks—rather than woos—women to punish them for his mother's rejection of him. "Don Juan, the world's great cad, was deserted by his mother early in childhood," Dr. Karl Menninger explained. "He spent his entire life treating other women in exactly the same way that his mother treated him, first making them love him and then leaving them."

The classic example was Casanova, the Italian rake who claimed to have had affairs with more than 1100 women, a score that was not disputed by contemporaries. From all accounts, Casanova was a magnetic, witty, highly intelligent rogue who possessed a variety of talents that exceeded his accomplishments in the boudoir. He was the illegitimate son of an occasional actress who found steadier employment as a prostitute. When his mother set up housekeeping with paramours, the boy was farmed out to neighbors in Venice who mistreated and half-starved him. Selected to study for the priesthood, he was expelled from the seminary for "scandalous and immoral conduct" at the precocious age of sixteen and embarked on a series of incredible adventures throughout Europe.

When reduced to working by the collapse of a quick-rich scheme, Casanova made a living as a journalist, preacher, violinist, abbot, diplomat, bodyguard, businessman and gambler. His audacity was matched by his glibness. He persuaded Clement XIII to award him the papal order of the Golden Spur in spite of his earlier indiscretions at the seminary. Imprisoned as a spy in Venice, he made a daring escape to Paris with the help of a bribed official. Every nobleman in France was conniving for the appointment as director of the state lottery, which was more lucrative than a license to steal, but Louis XV gave the plum to the foreign fugitive. When irregularities in the lottery were exposed, Casanova skipped to Russia at the invitation of Catherine the Great, an eager acolyte in the arts of love. The old scoundrel never lost his touch. He still had access to some exclusive boudoirs when he died in 1798 at the age of seventy-three.

Although Casanova slept with many women who could have helped him in high places, practically all of his amours were one-night stands. That always betrays the Don Juan's self-doubts. He must kiss and run, because he cannot permit a woman to compare his performances in bed and discover his inadequacy after the first night. He never can have an intimate relationship with any woman, because he associates her with his incestuous feeling for his mother, who denied him the love he wanted. His conquests are nothing more than brief occupations of forbidden terrritory, for he must flee from the guilt of his illicit lust.

Another form of self-doubt that can be traced to an Oedipal conflict impels a middle-aged man to divorce his wife after fifteen or twenty years and marry a younger woman on the rebound. "The men usually are going through a phase that can be called the denial of reality," Dr. Nyswander says. "It is related to the fear that aging is accompanied by a loss of virility. Every psychiatrist sees a steady flow of such men at the urging of marriage counselors and members of the family who hope that the husband will listen to reason and drop the idea of a divorce.

"The cases follow such a typical pattern that the details are interchangeable. I have just finished talking to a forty-six-year-old lawyer who has four children and a wife in her early forties. He admits that he was happy with her until a nineteen-year-old secretary at the office caught his eye. One thing led to another, they began an affair, and then he told his wife out of the blue that he was in love with the girl and wanted a divorce.

"Listening to him was like hearing the playback of an old, familiar record. You can anticipate what a middle-aged husband who is on the defensive for abandoning his wife is going to say. They all insist that sex has nothing to do with their decision to get a divorce. They always put the young woman's attraction on the social level.

"'She makes me feel vital again,' they tell you. 'My wife hasn't grown intellectually. All she is interested in are the kids and the house. This girl knows what's going on in the world. She can discuss politics, world affairs, books, the theater. I never realized I had been in such a rut until I met her. I feel like an awful heel about my wife, but the kids are old enough to understand that some of the best years of my life are ahead of me. I'm too young to sit around like a bump on a log and listen to my arteries harden.'

"Three phrases are repeated constantly: 'I'm really in love with the girl. . . . Sex is only incidental to the way I feel about her. . . . I'm still a young man.' Like Shakespeare's lady who protested too much, the men are trying to suppress the truth to themselves. The complete male does not have to convince anyone of his virility—especially himself."

A middle-aged man tips his hand more obviously than he realizes in declaring that he is not marrying a young girl for her sexual appeal. He really is seeking a partner who will not be critical of his declining potency. He thinks it will be easier for him to gratify an inexperienced girl than a mature woman whose libido has been educated by marriage—and he is right. A girl who marries a man twenty or thirty years older has deep psychological problems herself. She, too, is looking for an easy out from the sexual demands of a young husband. She does not want to be a wife and a mother. She hopes, subconsciously, to be a young widow with no responsibilities.

Some primitive tribes sacrificed elderly members to appease the evil spirits of death and divert them from claiming younger victims. Casting off a middle-aged wife is the modern equivalent of this rite for a man who has a morbid fear of aging and sees in his wife a constant reminder that his life span is diminishing. The healthy, well-adjusted person accepts the inevitability of death and can even derive great satisfaction from attaining certain milestones of advancing years.

Often a man who is delighted by the birth of his first grandchild will say teasingly to his wife, "I've never slept with a grandmother before." An immature man who resents his new grandparental status for its implications of old age looks at his wife's wrinkles, aging figure and gray—or dyed—hair and mutters to himself, "My God, she looks as old as my mother." That sets off a chain reaction of Oedipal guilt that transforms marital intercourse into an incestuous relationship. He cannot function sexually with his wife, a substitute mother, because he shrinks in revulsion from violating the incest taboo.

A man suffering from this fixation is fully potent only with prostitutes or lower-class women who are not associated in his mind with the mother figure. He may go through the preliminary stages of coitus with his wife, but he ejaculates prematurely to terminate the incestuous act before he defiles her with his sperm.

It is an interesting footnote to the civil rights movement in the United States that the first integrated places of public accommodation in the deep South were fancy brothels patronized by white clients. Negro girls were available for gentlemen who were inhibited with "respectable" women of the same social status as their mothers. Such establishments still flourish. It also is an open secret that some rabid members of the Ku Klux Klan and other white supremacy groups keep mulatto mistresses. The quickest way to make a segregationist's hackles rise is to ask why there has been no reduction in the number of mulatto babies born annually in the South despite the vigorous prosecution of Negro men for rape or even the suspicion of it.

A strange characteristic of the Oedipus complex is that it frequently does not crop up until middle age. Some husbands, for example, suddenly are repelled by their wives' pubic hair and insist that they shave the genital area. This eccentricity is touched off by an association of ideas that goes back to a man's long dormant childhood memory of seeing his mother naked and the shock of discovering that she did not have a phallus. His mother's pubic hair made an indelible impression on him, because he thought it was a growth to cover the shameful scar of her castration. By making his wife shave her pelvis, he creates the delusion of having sexual intercourse with a young girl who cannot be identified with his mother.

Although the link between sexual maladjustment and alcoholism was established a long time ago, public attention has been focused on the effect rather than the cause of excessive drinking. Alcoholics Anonymous and other agencies have softpedaled the sexual aspects of the problem in their publicity, on the valid grounds that references to impotence and homosexuality will scare off prospective members. In recent years, however, doctors treating alcoholics privately and in group therapy have been probing deeply into the libidinal histories of their patients.

In 1964, three psychiatrists in Massachusetts published a report on thirty-seven cases of wife beating—one of the nasty by-products of alcoholism—referred to them by the courts. The doctors found that the husbands and wives fell into definite patterns. The men were "shy, sexually ineffectual mothers' boys." The women were "aggressive, efficient, masculine and sexually frigid." The wife generally dominated the husband until he had one drink too many and insisted on his conjugal rights. The woman, whose father usually had been a wife beater, resisted, and in the ensuing battle both parties relieved their frustrations. "The periods of violent behavior by the husband served to release him momentarily from his anxiety about his ineffectiveness as a man," the doctors noted, "while giving his wife apparent masochistic gratification and helping probably to deal with the guilt arising from the intense hostility expressed in her controlling, castrating behavior." The conclusion was that the couple needed "a frequent alternation of passive and aggressive roles to achieve a working equilibrium." Some marriages are made in heaven; others in the sexual inadequacies of wretched partners.

Why do men drink? Dr. A. A. Brill, a pioneer who treated alcoholics psychiatrically, concluded that they were consumed by jealousy, because they were convinced that their wives were unfaithful to them. "I explained the jealousy by the relative or absolute impotence which is encountered so often in this disease. For when I asked some of these patients how they knew that their wives had other men, they frequently admitted that they had no direct evidence but that they were nevertheless sure of it because they were not sufficiently stimulated by their wives. As one of them expressed it: 'If she did not run around with other men, she would be in need of sex and then would be anxious to excite me sexually.' In other words, he blamed his wife for his impotence. . . .

"In studying such cases we find that the patients invariably wish to run away from heterosexuality. Every chronic alcoholic studied by me either never attained genitality and object-finding or there was some noticeable weakness in his development which led sooner or later to a regression to the oral autoerotic phase. Some gave histories of bad experiences with women, unhappy marriages or love affairs for which they invariably blamed the women. Their excuse for excessive drinking is that they are lonesome and seek companionship in bar rooms or clubs. And, as is known, the homosexual element is glaringly displayed in such gatherings whether they are of the upper or lower strata of society."

To illustrate the extremes to which an alcoholic will go to create rivals through fantasy, Brill cited the case of a man who was convinced that his wife, a former fat lady in a circus, was deceiving him. He claimed that she drugged his food so that she could meet her lover while he was asleep. He locked her room every night, but he insisted that she slipped out through the window. When Brill pointed out that the woman weighed 450 pounds and hardly could get through the window frame, the husband retorted, "The guy must be strong enough to move the whole wall."

Dr. Ruth Fox, medical director of the National Council on Alcoholism, agrees that sexual problems are a major cause of excessive drinking, which in turn aggravates the situation. "The incidence of homosexuality, philandering and impotence among alcoholics is much higher than the general population," she says. "Their divorce rate is four times higher. They drink to bolster their ego, but alcohol is a depressant that impairs their sexual capability, and a vicious circle is set in motion. The wives of alcoholics commonly complain of their husbands' sexual inadequacy. Further questioning reveals that there was dissatisfaction on that score long before the men started to hit the bottle hard.

"One of the reasons many men fall off the wagon after they seem to have been cured of the disease is that their wives refuse to resume sexual relations with them. The women were so disgusted by their husbands' behavior while they were drinking that they want no part of them, or they were so disappointed in them as sexual partners that they don't want to go through the frustrating experience again."

All obsessive drives are accompanied by a loss of libido, whether the compulsion is for liquor, narcotics, gambling, work or food. "The next time you are in a good restaurant, look around and you will see that the majority of the customers are middle-aged," Dr. Nyswander comments. "The fact that they are the group that can best afford the high prices is immaterial. As men and women grow older, interest in food replaces their waning sexual desire. When sex, the adult's greatest pleasure, is curtailed, he regresses to eating, the greatest pleasure in infancy. The whole thing is simply the substitution of one gratification for another."

Perhaps the most conclusive evidence supporting Freud's Oedipus theory is furnished by studies of compulsive gambling —a disease that rarely was treated successfully until a few years ago. Dr. Harry Perlowitz, a Brooklyn psychiatrist, has worked with more than two hundred patients as a consultant to Gamblers Anonymous, an organization patterned after Alcoholics Anonymous.

"Every compulsive gambler I've ever seen grew up in a disturbed family environment," Dr. Perlowitz reports. "His parents were divorced or so incompatible that he was denied the love a child needs for emotional stability. Another common characteristic is a strong attachment to the mother despite—or perhaps because of—her rejection of him. She usually was a domineering, self-centered woman who discouraged affection, intensifying the child's sense of insecurity and resulting in a dependency relationship which continued into adult life.

"Unlike other addictions, gambling leaves no obvious physical scars. That is why it is so difficult to detect. Quite often, a wife and members of the immediate family are not aware that a man has been a compulsive gambler for ten or fifteen years until he gets into trouble with the law. The typical victim is a gay, personable fellow who tells amusing stories with a flair cultivated by inventing lies to borrow money to feed his betting fever. His intelligence is above average, and he generally earns a good salary until he gets into a mess for neglecting his job or stealing money from his company.

"Money has only one use for a compulsive gambler. It is an instrument for buying love. If he won the first prize in the Irish Sweepstakes, he would try immediately to increase his bankroll to command more love. He has no confidence in his ability to sustain it on any other basis. As a rule, his sex drive is very low, because it is not an expression of his love."

Operators of race tracks, casinos and bookie joints welcome the compulsive gambler with loud, gladsome cries, for he is certain to wind up a loser. He consistently bets on hopeless long shots and ridiculous propositions such as five-horse parlays even yokels recognize as sucker bait. He gambles so foolishly that it seems he is playing subconsciously to lose.

"Of course he is," Dr. Perlowitz says. "He wants to punish himself for defiling his mother's love by trying to purchase it as though she is a prostitute, and he compounds his guilt by making his family suffer for his corrupt conduct. Yet he will break his neck doing favors for total strangers to gain the approval he wants so desperately."

The early forties are an especially critical period for a man who attaches exaggerated importance to the numbers game. The normal attrition of age, combined with accumulating financial and psychological pressures, may cause a noticeable drop in his rate of coitus, arousing his wholly unfounded suspicion that he is slipping into impotence or, worse yet, homosexuality. It is astonishing how many men secretly fear that they are latent homosexuals. And it is alarming how often mature men who never before have shown a predisposition for sexual deviations suddenly succumb to them rather than face the reality of physiological changes in middle age.

Men with the most admirable attributes of character—integrity, altruism, courage, intelligence—have been driven to homosexuality by the false fear of impotence. It has happened to Nobel prize winners in literature and eminent composers, to clergymen and educators, to high-ranking cabinet members and legislators. The transformation is so unexpected that even specialists misinterpret the symptoms.

Medical circles in New York recently were thrown into a tailspin by a highly successful surgeon who had been married more than twenty years and had two children. His colleagues, including staff psychiatrists who saw him every day at the hospital where he operated, were amused when he began displaying photographs of his newly decorated apartment as though he was a proud father showing off pictures of a new baby. Some doctors turn to painting for self-expression; others play with amateur orchestras. Friends assumed he had taken up interior decorating as a rather odd hobby, but they did not suspect something murky was going on until they compared notes and it dawned upon them that the pictures were of an apartment with a strange layout.

Cautious questioning revealed that the surgeon had left his wife and two children and was living with a younger man, a flaming homosexual who was a clerk in a Third Avenue antique shop. They had met while the surgeon was looking, ironically, for a wedding anniversary gift for his wife. The clerk was so helpful that the surgeon invited him for a drink in a bar next door, unaware that it was a notorious hangout for the "gay" crowd. The atmosphere of the place and the effete youths who frequented it intrigued the surgeon. The upshot was that he got drunk and encouraged the clerk's advances. When he sobered up and realized what had happened, he reacted like a guilty child who wants to be punished for his misbehavior by calling attention to it. He went out of his way to humiliate his wife by appearing with his companion where he was sure to be seen. Showing pictures of the apartment to people who knew him socially was part of the pattern. After his chief at the hospital warned him that he would lose his operating privileges if he did not conduct himself properly, he brought on his dismissal by making a deliberate play for an orderly.

Associates offered to arrange psychiatric treatment for him, but he angrily refused their help. The clue to the mystery was provided by his wife. She confided to friends that he had been brooding over his declining potency and that they had not slept together for more than a year before he sought a new catalyst for his libido.

Although it is difficult to believe this, some agents of the Federal Bureau of Narcotics insist that there are more male than female prostitutes in New York, Philadelphia, Chicago and Los Angeles. A high percentage of young drug addicts lend themselves to sexual perversions to get the $20 to $40 a day they need to support the habit. They openly solicit older men who can afford to pay well for services rendered.

One sign of incipient homosexuality in middle age is a sudden preoccupation with clothes and fastidious grooming. This deviation is known as narcissism, a term suggested by the legend of the handsome Greek youth who was so enamored of his reflection in a pool that Echo, a nymph, pined away with unrequited love for him.

Narcissism is a regression to the period when a child's emotions are totally centered around his "magical and adored self." It is natural—and necessary—for parents to praise a child's appearance, but possessive mothers carry it to such extremes that a young boy is often led to believe that favorable acceptance is predicated entirely upon his physical attractiveness. If he does not outgrow this stage, he may be able to love only someone as much like himself as possible—a person of the same sex.

A clear distinction must be made between men who have always had a flair for good clothes and those who first evince an interest in them in middle age. It would be absurd to imply that every well-dressed man is effeminate. There are men who derive a genuine sense of esthetic pleasure from expensive suits and haberdashery. In such rugged lines of work as law enforcement, politics and heavy construction, men who have climbed to the top traditionally advertise their affluence and authority with dapper wardrobes.

Until the Industrial Revolution forced the adoption of functional attire, gentlemen of quality cut more elegant figures than women. "History proves beyond all doubt that fine clothes originated with man, not woman," Pearl Binder notes in *The Peacock's Tail,* a study of fashions. "It was from man that woman subsequently borrowed all her sartorial glamor. It was man who originally wore long hair, corsets, ribbons and lace, high-heeled shoes, feathers and jewels, muffs and fans."

In this age of buttoned-down conformity, however, something more urgent than vanity suddenly impels a man to pay inordinate attention to his clothes and grooming. He is overly sensitive about the loss of his physical and sexual attractiveness and tries to compensate for it by reverting to the meticulous habits that brought him compliments as a child.

Narcissism is the principal reason many handsome, well-built men drift into homosexuality or impotence in middle age. Their overevaluation of physical appearance causes them to fear that women will expect more than they can deliver, so they unconsciously shy away from sexual encounters that will expose their imagined inadequacy.

A less obvious, but equally significant, indication is a gradual withdrawal from women into activities with "the boys." The usual excuse is that men are better cardplayers and golfers and more interesting conversationalists than women. That may be true, yet anyone who has listened in on bull sessions in bars and locker rooms hardly can claim it was an enlightening experience. A man's description of his approach shot on the fourteenth hole can be just as stupefying as a woman's recital of her latest household crisis.

The fact that the boys go in for virile pastimes, two-fisted drinking and salty language is purely window dressing for their evasion of women. As Dr. A. A. Brill suggested earlier, there is an undertone of homosexuality in the hearty camaraderie, the inside jokes and the fussing with arrangements for poker games and golf foursomes, all of which are no different from the twittery anticipation of spinsters planning a sightseeing bus tour.

It is not a coincidence that the regulars who congregate in restaurants that cater to the sporting crowd are comprised largely of confirmed bachelors and divorced or separated men. Despite their pretense of hairy-chested virility, the blunt truth is that they feel they are washouts with women. They generally appear with statuesque girls, but their dates are strictly social accessories, like the fancy cuff links they affect. More often than not, the girls are given cab fare and sent home while the boys debate far into the night whether Joe Louis could have licked Cassius Clay or Mickey Mantle could have carried Babe Ruth's bat.

Obviously, weekly poker sessions or an occasional fishing trip are innocent diversions. The danger is that they may gradually lead to a breakdown in social, then sexual, intercourse. One definition of intercourse is communication. When husbands and wives stop communicating, they eventually stop sharing the same bed.

Apathy, not age, is the chief enemy of the male libido. Sexual desire in a mature man is more the product of mental than physical excitation. A man who cuts himself off from the stimulation of women may be sexually senescent at the age of thirty, but if he maintains social contacts with women the odds are heavily in his favor of leading a fairly active sex life, granted reasonably good health, at seventy.

Some years ago I observed at close range the late Prince Aly Khan during an interlude that was accurately described by gossip columnists as a torrid affair with a Hollywood star.

This happened while I was ghostwriting Elsa Maxwell's auto-biography, *R.S.V.P.* One day she peremptorily announced to Aly that she and I were moving into his showplace on the Riviera, the Château de l'Horizon near Cannes, as his house-guests. It was a ploy by Elsa to balk an invitation from Aly to the Duchess of Windsor with whom she was feuding, but that's another story.

Aly had just been divorced from Rita Hayworth and was back in circulation reaffirming his reputation as a great lover —a distinction he eminently deserved judging from the affectionate references to him by women with whom he had been involved romantically. Aly was not given to one-night stands. When he was infatuated with a woman, the affair usually lasted many months and his other amours were so curtailed that he was practically an anchorite by the standards of the international playboy set.

In his pursuit of glamorous sexpots Aly, then in his middle forties, had bagged an impressive collection of prize trophies. Although he had enormous charm, his appeal to women was a subject of endless conjecture to people with nothing better to do. He was a short, balding man who spoke in a high-pitched singsong and abused the millionaire's privilege of dressing like a refugee from Skid Row. All sorts of preposterous yarns were concocted to explain his amatory prowess. According to one story, he dipped his hands up to the wrists in a champagne bucket filled with ice water while he was making love to retard his own response until he had brought the lady to a series of climaxes.

One afternoon Aly gave a buffet lunch for two hundred guests in his formal garden overlooking the Mediterranean. Among them was an old flame, an American who had left her husband after meeting Aly and had then married on the rebound one of the wealthiest industrialists in the British Empire. She was sitting by herself watching Aly dance with the homely, elderly wife of a local official. I had known her first husband and used that as a gambit to talk to her about Aly. She was the outspoken type who would give a candid answer to an impertinent question.

"Would women go for Aly if he didn't have an exotic title and an allowance of a million dollars a year from the Aga Khan?" I asked.

"Of course," she said. "Look at him." Aly was pressing his flustered partner against him, bending her backward gently from the waist and gazing intently into her eyes. "Aly acts that way with every woman, whether she's a fat old grandmother or a stunning girl. Everything about women fascinates Aly. He loves the way they dress, walk, talk, think. He'll watch you pull on a pair of stockings or fix your make-up and go into raptures, as though he's never seen anything so wonderfully feminine before. When you're with him, he makes you feel that no other woman on earth exists for him."

"But it never lasts," I said. "Doesn't she realize Aly will react just as passionately to another woman as soon as he leaves her?"

She smiled pensively. "That's the hellish part of it. But at least you've had that moment of—of complete adoration. That's more than most women ever know."

# 4

# The Brink of Arousal

\* \* \*

EVER SINCE WOMEN ACQUIRED THE POWER OF SPEECH THEY
have complained that one thing is on men's minds constantly. The generalization is closer to the mark than most of
the broadsides the ladies customarily fire at their favorite targets. Sex is, indeed, in the forefront of the virile male's consciousness, because he is more susceptible than a woman to a
wide variety of erotic stimuli that keeps him on the brink of
arousal.

These flashes of desire are like the tiles in a complicated
mosaic. Separately, each is a minuscule fragment of the overall design; put together, they form a pattern that is an important factor in offsetting the erosive effects of age on the libido
of a man past forty. They also are a major source of the
friction that alienates middle-aged couples after years of sexual compatibility.

Hardly a husband alive has never been accused by his wife
of a puerile obsession with sex at one time or another. The
indictment usually charges him with harping on Topic A and
foolish capering in the presence of other women. Some waspish wives rant as though men are guilty of turning every social
gathering into a fertility rite, but even amiable women are
apt to go into peevish harangues at the onset of the menopause, when they are depressed by anxiety of their fading sexual appeal.

It is a commentary rather than a criticism to say that
women are constitutionally incapable of understanding that the

normal male always is on the qui vive sexually until age or a functional disorder retires him from the chase. It is a pardonable blind spot, for there is no parallel in the female's behavior pattern to the male's immediate reaction to the slightest titillation—the glimpse of a woman's thigh when she crosses her legs, the curve of a breast, a provocative wiggle. Women are disciplined to resist casual sexual excitement for reasons that are more compelling than considerations of morality.

When the spirit moves her, a woman responds to the call of the wild as impulsively as a man. Wives surprised in compromising situations rarely bear bruises attesting that they were subdued forcibly while resisting the vile embraces of seducers, and few girls are deflowered against their will in premarital affairs. The libido of both sexes operates on the same circuit, but it is activated by separate psychological switches.

The difference between male and female responses to eroticism can be reduced to a simple rule of thumb: A man reacts to what he sees, a woman to what she hears. This subtle distinction, like all basic attitudes toward sex, reflects the dominant influence of social conditioning.

Every culture has imposed more restraints on the sexual conduct of women since the concept of permanent family relationships was accepted by primitive man. Then, as now, taboos on promiscuity were adopted to protect the female from the shameful consequences of bearing illegitimate children. Although the double standard of morality has been relaxed since World War I, two short generations of greater sexual freedom have not liberated women from society's condemnation of the unwed mother.

Copulation and pregnancy are sanctioned by marriage, but it does not dispel completely the inhibitions and suspicions that are inculcated in a girl during adolescence. Subconsciously, she still has an atavistic fear that the male will abandon her callously after she has yielded to him. She wants to be told that love will sustain the union beyond the brief gratification of his physical desire.

The genesis of a woman's need for assurances of affection before she submits to a man is explained by Dr. Theodor Reik in *The Psychology of Sex Relations:* "Woman at first was only a sexual object to, and a co-worker with, man. Sexual intercourse was at first not very different from rape. The primitive man assaulted the woman ferociously and overpowered her. . . . Sex was originally accompanied by the aggressiveness, brutality and coarseness of the male, was a violent conquest of the female, who resisted with all her power. Women got rather a rough deal and were put on the defensive. . . .

"Refusal to surrender except on her own terms finally became an assurance to women against contempt and hostility, a guarantee that men would treat them well, would not scorn them and hurt their pride. . . . Their willingness in sex became the reward for the friendliness and kindness which man had to demonstrate beforehand. . . . The woman of today is not unlike the prehistoric woman in this regard. They are sisters under the skin. Has the situation radically changed? Indeed not. Today, as many thousands of years ago, women want to be loved before they surrender."

The see vs. hear formula for male and female responsiveness to erotic stimulation agrees in every detail with Kinsey's data for thirty-three different types of arousal. He found that only two categories, romantic novels and movies, had a stronger impact on women. The appeal of love stories to the female is obvious. The hero courts his heart's desire in more ardent and eloquent language than a woman ordinarily hears. She identifies with the heroine who resolutely refuses to succumb to the handsome devil panting for her favors until he professes his eternal devotion.

An interesting footnote on women's sensitivity to such arousal is provided by Dr. Malcolm J. Marks, a psychoanalyst. "A fairly common complication in the profession is the woman patient who falls in love with her analyst. The usual explanation is that he represents a father image to her, but I'm convinced that her attachment verges on a desire for a physical relationship with him. She actually believes the analyst is attempting to seduce her when he speaks of love in purely abstract terms. Such a transference is unknown between male patients and female analysts, because men accept love in a more impersonal frame of reference."

The art of making love to a woman is, preeminently, the expression of tenderness that gives her a feeling of security at the peak of her emotional vulnerability. "Women value the overture far more than the performance," Oswald Schwarz commented. An abrupt approach to a woman, even a wife who thoroughly enjoys intercourse with her husband, arouses her subliminal fear of brutal assault. The majority, married or single, resent a nonchalant, perfunctory pass, because it implies that her desirability is an accident of availability. Only prostitutes and nymphomaniacs consummate impromptu meetings in bed without preliminary assurance of considerate treatment.

Suggestive images trigger the male libido spontaneously, but women are offended by overt allusions to sex that, figuratively, strip them of their defenses before they are ready to surrender. A man's passion is inflamed by the sight of his nude wife after years of intimacy with her; once a woman's curiosity has been satisfied, she gets an erotic flutter from a man's naked body only when she is in a compliant mood. Coitus during the day or with a light on at night adds to a man's enjoyment; most women are inhibited by illumination and prefer the dark.

The genital aspects of sex hold no interest even for women who participate in perversions. There are no female counterparts of Peeping Toms or exhibitionists who expose themselves in public. Stripteasers and chorus girls who parade in costumes as revealing as the law allows cannot be compared to pathological exhibitionists. The theatrical performers get no libidinous thrill from displaying their bodies. They are, in fact, contemptuous of the customers who pay to ogle them. The audience for pornography and voyeurism is comprised exclusively of males. Virtually all the fetishes and other aberrations catalogued by Krafft-Ebing are practiced only by men.

The urban male constantly is exposed to visual impressions that intensify his awareness of sex. At work and in public places he is distracted at every turn by girls wearing sweaters two sizes too small and skirts so short that watching a woman sit in a chair or get out of a car is a war of nerves for both parties. He is immersed in the aura of the boudoir by newspaper and television ads for girdles, brassieres and feminine toiletries. Circumspect publications that once suppressed references to the female anatomy below the shoulders now report routinely the physical dimensions of Hollywood starlets and run pictures formerly found only in *The Police Gazette* and *Captain Billy's Whiz Bang.*

A married man does not have to look far for such fillips to his libido. They have been brought into his home by startling changes in matrimonial customs since the 1920's. The social upheaval after World War I witnessed an equally sharp break with so-called bourgeois conventions repressing the sex drive.

Modesty—or prudery, depending on the perspective—was the measure of feminine refinement during the Victorian era. Husbands rarely saw their wives nude or in a state of undress suggesting it. *Godey's Lady's Book,* the first woman's periodical in the United States, and similar English publications carried articles on procedures for disrobing at night so that wives would not reveal their "personal parts" to husbands. Even when a woman was in dishabille, she was swathed in a formidable layer of clothing—a camisole, a bulky petticoat, a whalebone corset extending from the armpits to the knees and full-length drawers—which made her as impregnable to amorous advances as an Iron Maiden. The prescribed attire for bed was a heavy flannel nightgown buttoned to the throat, and genteel ladies were advised to sleep with the knees firmly locked to prevent the garment from riding up above the lower limbs during the night.

It is astonishing, in retrospect, that strongly entrenched barriers to intimacy have been wiped out in a relatively short time by such developments as the trends to smaller homes and streamlined women's fashions. Cramped apartments have thrown married couples on all economic levels into closer physical contact than most slum families knew a half-century ago. Then, a middle-class wife prepared to retire for the night in the privacy of her dressing room or, at least, a bathroom that was big enough for a clothes compartment. Today, a woman limited to one bedroom closet thinks nothing of walking around in a skimpy girdle and bra in the presence of her husband, then stripping completely before getting into bed. Kinsey found that more than half the women born after 1910 sleep in the nude, and declining lingerie sales indicate the proportion is substantially higher now.

Since women are unaffected by visual stimulation, they often do not realize that their conjugal stripteases and casual displays of nudity spark erotic impulses that constantly charge a man's sexual battery. A simple comparison underscores this difference in psychological orientation. An experienced, thirty-year-old woman eager for her lover after passionate kisses still requires further arousal in foreplay before she is ready to receive him. A sexually active man in his sixties who suddenly sees an undressed woman needs no physical contact with her to carry on from there. He comes to a full erection immediately.

One reason why frequent intercourse helps to prolong a middle-aged man's potency is that it builds up a backlog of erotic memories that sustains the tone of his conditioned responses. As he grows older, he draws heavily on past incidents and the vivid images they evoke to counteract the effect of age on his sexuality. Since Freud, everyone who has investigated the phenomenon has agreed that sexual fantasies occur far more frequently among men than women and invariably are more intense.

Dreams are the acting-out of repressed desires, but a woman never casts off all her inhibitions even in sleep. She may dream she is in a romantic setting with a movie star who is kissing and caressing her, but she stops short of projecting herself into coitus with him. A man meets more passionate partners in his dreams; he sees himself in new and exciting preliminaries that lead up to unconventional positions in intercourse. Sometimes his sensations are so acute that when he awakens he imagines he can still feel the texture of his phantom partner's skin, taste her mouth, smell her body and hear her ecstatic cries as he thrusts into her.

Although nocturnal emissions are generally associated with adolescence, it is not unusual for a man well past fifty to have an orgasm in his sleep, especially when he has been isolated from feminine contacts for an extended period. Women reach climaxes in dreams so rarely, however, that few experience more than one or two nocturnal experiences throughout their lives.

Positive proof of the male's recurrent sexual fantasies from puberty until old age are the morning erections with which the great majority of males regularly awaken—including those who are impotent in other circumstances. Doctors once attributed these spontaneous arousals to the accumulation of urine in the bladder during the night, supposedly resulting in pressures that cause the nerves in the penis to tighten. Urologists of the old school, who find organic functions easier to explain than psychological processes, still hold to the bladder theory despite its obvious flaws. If the delayed need to go to the bathroom produced erections, it would be a simple matter to cure impotent patients by telling them not to urinate for several hours before attempting intercourse. Another glaring contradiction is the fact that a man does not come to an erection automatically when he is unable to relieve himself. On the contrary, the congestion tends to make tumescence more difficult.

Morning erections are the products of dreams that are safety valves for repressed forms of sexuality and aggression. Many mature men are secretly ashamed of their fantasies and periodically worry that they are turning into degenerates, but libidinous dreams are as universal as breathing—and as necessary for maintaining psychic equilibrium. The normal—that is, the well-adjusted—man attracted to women who are unapproachable because of his moral or social scruples appeases his desire by possessing them in his dreams. The neurotic, who has weaker control of his crude sex drive, acts out his dreams and tries to possess a woman physically in violation of all restrictions.

A man's incestuous conflicts are resolved in dreams without reproaches of the conscience in imaginary intercourse with women who closely resemble his mother or sister. Dream sequences often are remarkably vivid. Faces and such details as breasts and positions in coitus are seen distinctly. Upon awakening, a man can repeat long conversations and recall the exact amount of a dinner check, a cab ride to a rendezvous and the furnishings of the room.

Sexual hallucinations are not confined to sleep. They occur daily during conscious moments. A strange woman putting on lipstick in a restaurant may give a man visions of her in mouth-genital contacts with him or other sophisticated techniques his wife is unwilling to practice. Some men undress women mentally while they are walking along the street. Others never tire of a game they play shortly before dropping off to sleep. They review all the women with whom they have had sexual experiences and invent an endless variety of categories—physical characteristics, single or married, color of hair, impromptu or planned affairs, geographical locations—to conjure up old memories.

A man's five senses constitute, in effect, a radar that picks up random sexual references and converts them into erotic images through the process of association. A girl in a crowd who resembles someone he knew twenty years ago will start the wheels of reminiscence spinning. A mortgage installment may slip his mind, but he never forgets the amorous connotation a locale, a song, a perfume or the turn of a phrase holds for him.

The most dramatic evidence of the profound psychological impact of past sexual experience is provided by men who have suffered castration as a result of accidents, war injuries or mutilation. Most people assume that the loss of the testicles renders a man impotent, a belief that goes back to ancient times when the ultimate masculine indignity was inflicted on prisoners of war. Actually, men who are castrated after reaching maturity are capable of coitus for periods ranging up to twenty years.

By the time he is twenty-five, a man has been responding to sexual excitation with erections for at least ten years. The pattern is established so firmly in the areas of the brain controlling the erection center that it continues to react to familiar stimuli after emasculation. It is even possible for castrates to achieve orgasms, although the ejaculate is sterile. Their rates of intercourse are considerably lower than the incidence of unimpaired men, but the remembrance of things past compensates in a surprising degree for the lack of sex hormones that normally sustain the libido.

The seductive creatures who populate a man's fantasies are no threat to a wife—provided she remains in the composite picture by contributing fresh images to it. Marriage dulls a man's anticipation of intercourse with his wife only when the couple follows a rigid routine that merely produces the minimum arousal sufficient to complete the act. The middle-aged man who jumps the reservation after fifteen or twenty years of fidelity is not seeking new bed-mates so much as new experiences to recharge his sex drive. In the great majority of cases he still loves his wife and wants to cling to their marriage, but she refuses to believe it, because she has no interest herself in a variety of partners.

An extramarital affair always seems to be a wonderful idea

at the moment to a man, but a woman's deeper emotional involvement with sex impels her to hold out for an affinity that carries the promise of enduring beyond a one-night stand. Strangely enough, the female's desire for a permanent relationship applies equally to homosexual liaisons. Male deviates are notorious for changing partners constantly, but it is not unusual for Lesbians to form lifelong attachments more binding than conventional marriages.

The importance of understanding—and making reciprocal adjustments to—conflicting male and female attitudes toward sex is all the more apparent when their reactions to erotic arousal are compared. Many problems of sexual incompatability that estrange middle-aged couples stem from ignorance of the psychological factor in marital relations, for there is conclusive evidence that despite anatomical differences, the physical responses of both sexes during coitus are almost identical.

More than twelve thousand controlled tests along these lines were conducted at the Washington University School of Medicine in St. Louis between 1954 and 1965 under the supervision of Dr. William H. Masters, a gynecologist, and Mrs. Virginia E. Johnson, a psychologist. Their unique study is, by all odds, the most authoritative clinical investigation of sex ever made.

All other sexual surveys have been based largely on personal interviews, an unsatisfactory scientific method on several counts. Most people are reluctant to reveal the complete details of their sex lives to strangers. Even when they believe they are telling the truth their memory is apt to be faulty. Statistics compiled from questionnaires are suspect, because men tend to exaggerate, and women to understate, their rates of coitus and degree of satisfaction. Further, test subjects hardly can give objective appraisals of their physical sensations and emotional involvement while in the throes of sexual excitement.

These obstacles to accurate analyses of the effects of sexual stimulation were eliminated by the revolutionary procedure employed in the Washington University project. A total of 312 men and 382 women between the ages of eighteen and eighty-nine permitted staff members to make direct observations of them during coitus and masturbation. In addition, color movies were taken to show the tumescence of primary and secondary sex organs during the cycle of arousal. Special instruments also recorded body changes in four successive stages—early and intense excitement, the orgasm and the post-orgasmic phase.

The experiments indicated that in the first three stages both sexes go through physical processes that are remarkably similar. The male's erection is matched by an enlargement of the female's genital structure. Her clitoris, a homologue of the penis, doubles in size; the length and lateral distention of her vagina expand about 50 percent; the labia of her vulva are so engorged that they double in size. There also is marked swelling of the female's breasts. Her first response to sexual excitement is an erection of the nipples, and just before an orgasm her breasts increase about 25 percent in size. Similarly, sexual activity produces a hardening of the nipples in most men.

The one marked difference throughout the cycle is the last phase, after an orgasm. A man's desire for further love-making falls off immediately, whereas a woman can be brought to another climax within a few seconds. In most cases she remains on a high level of excitation for several hours and, if properly manipulated, can have at least one orgasm—and perhaps as many as six—before a man can raise a satisfactory erection again. Many explanations have been offered to account for this discrepancy, but sexologists do not agree on the answer.

Opposing theories center around the fact that a woman does not ejaculate during an orgasm. The prostate gland and seminal vesicles, which are the sources of the male's semen, are only vestigial structures in the female. Some specialists argue that the male's ejaculation is so violent that it depletes him completely. Others contend that an orgasm is such a soaring emotional experience for a woman that her exhilaration extends beyond the brief release of maximum tension. Washington University has not looked into the cause of this variance in postorgasmic reactions, but it has come up with a good deal of pertinent information on a more important question— the matter of the difference in the time it takes men and women to reach an orgasm.

There is no physiological basis for the often repeated statement that a woman is much slower than a man in coming to a climax. Stopwatch tests at Washington University show a negligible variation in normal male and female responses to the initiation of direct physical stimulation. The male comes to an erection within five seconds. The female's corresponding reaction, vaginal lubrication, occurs within thirty seconds. Thereafter, well-adjusted partners advance smoothly through mounting levels of tension to almost simultaneous orgasms in two or three minutes.

A few guarded references to the fast orgasms reached by women during masturbation have been made by researchers at Washington University. Kinsey, who explored the subject thoroughly, found that married women who were consistently frustrated by their husbands' ineffectual love-making masturbated to orgasms in less than three minutes, which is just about the average time for the male to ejaculate in coitus.

When a mature couple has persistent difficulty in coordinating their orgasms, the trouble invariably is some form of impotence on one side of the bed—the husband's premature ejaculation or the wife's frigidity. Well-mated partners occasionally have disappointing episodes when one of them is overtired or under an emotional strain, but there are people who have been married twenty or thirty years and rarely, if ever, reach orgasms together. The failure usually is blamed on the man's inept love-making or his disregard for the woman's slower cycle of arousal, but there generally are more serious problems that need correction.

Dr. Marie Nyswander tells of a woman who was referred to her and announced, with self-righteous indignation, that twenty-two years of marriage to a wealthy dress manufacturer had driven her to the verge of a nervous breakdown. Her satisfactory experiences in bed with him could be counted "on the fingers of one hand," she claimed, and it was all due to his selfishness. When they had intercourse, he never held back his orgasm until she was near one herself. He was interested only in gratifying his own pleasure and left her so frustrated that she was unable to fall asleep for several hours. Dr. Nyswander asked approximately how long after they were joined her husband came to an orgasm.

"About forty or fifty minutes," she answered.

Dr. Nyswander thought the woman had misunderstood the question. "I mean, after he mounts and enters you, how soon does he ejaculate?"

"I just told you," she said impatiently. "Forty, maybe fifty, minutes."

People often lose all concept of time during intercourse. Dr. Nyswander asked the woman how she was able to pinpoint the span so precisely.

"We turn off the lights after the twelve o'clock news on the radio or at one o'clock if there's a good movie on TV. When he wants it, he starts to paw me right away, so if I'm not too tired I give in or else he'll pester me all night."

"How much time is spent in foreplay?"

"A few seconds. I don't like him to touch me that way and slobber over me with kisses. I know how long it takes, because I'm so nervous after he's finished that I turn on the light to read, and there's a clock on the night table."

Dr. Nyswander tried to tell the woman that her husband performed prodigies of self-control in holding off his orgasm, for coitus normally is consummated in two to five minutes.

The woman clearly was frigid, but when Dr. Nyswander suggested that she needed psychiatric treatment, she stormed out of the office and never returned. The strange part of the whole thing was that the husband, who was known in his business as a hard-boiled, irritable man, had submitted meekly to his wife's sullen conduct in bed for twenty-two years.

The study of sex is much like following the production of a play from the inception of the idea through the rewriting of the script, the casting, unforeseen headaches in rehearsals, staging problems and tryouts on the road to the nerve-racking opening on Broadway. The venture is studded with so many potential disasters it is a wonder that the vehicle ever comes alive and survives the verdict of the first-night critics. The mood of a performance on the stage or in bed can be ruined by an awkward gesture or a missed cue, for the expression of the libido is the most complicated process in the range of human activity.

Unlike most reactions, sexual desire does not originate in one center of the brain. It is triggered by an intricate network of many specialized areas that coordinate the impulses through the spinal cord to a group of nerve cells called the erection center in both men and women. From there, the impulses are transmitted to the penis or the clitoris, but virtually all parts of the body are involved as excitement builds to an orgasm.

Body heat rises to facilitate rapid and intense chemical changes in every cell. The pituitary, thyroid, adrenal, salivary and sweat glands speed up production. The hair literally stands on end; it actually takes on added tone. Blood pressure more than doubles with increasing tumescence, not only of the sex organs but of the lips and ear lobes. The pulse rate, normally between seventy and eighty per minute, shoots up to 150 —the peak of a sprinter's effort when he hits the tape in a 100-yard dash. Breathing is so labored that the partners look as though they are undergoing excruciating torture. As the climax approaches, there is a partial, sometimes total, loss of hearing, sight, touch, taste and smell. The explosive release is so overwhelming that there may be a blackout for a few seconds in what the French call *la mort douce* (the sweet death).

This anatomy of an orgasm is as one-dimensional as the blueprint of a building showing only the facade. If the physical factor alone was decisive, mutual gratification would be virtually assured once a man and a woman join in coitus, since they conform to identical patterns of response. Unfortunately, the sweet death may be the kiss of death to a relationship between people who are in rapport except on one crucial issue: They do not realize that the sexes vibrate to different psychological wavelengths.

Havelock Ellis coined a term, poly-erotic, to explain the conflict in men between abiding love for their wives and the sexual attraction other women hold for them. "The people who discuss whether men are more polygamic than women really mean more *poly-erotic*," he wrote in *Psychology of Sex*. "That is to say, not whether they desire more marriages but more sexual freedom. Women are fully as well able as men to experience affection for more than one person of the opposite sex, though on account of the deeper significance of sex for women they may be instinctively more fastidious than men in sexual choice, and on account of social and other considerations more reticent and cautious than men in manifesting or yielding to their affections."

When Ellis advanced this opinion in 1933, a decade after sex had become an acceptable conversation piece, it was distorted into a gambit to attack monogamous marriage as an "unnatural" institution. Pseudointellectuals argued that fidelity to one mate was incompatible with the male animal's voracious sexual appetite and led to repressions that were more harmful than the unbridled gratification of his desires. Such claptrap impressed no one except young bohemians, who had recently discovered sex, and "progressive" thinkers, who were three thousand years behind the times.

Monogamy is not a moral precept austere reformers arbitrarily imposed on man. He accepted it voluntarily early in our social evolution, because he recognized that a permanent union with one woman was the arrangement best suited for refining his physical urge into a more mature emotional relationship. Throughout history, many civilized and primitive people have approved polygamy. It was practiced with religious sanction by the ancient Hebrews, Egyptians, Chinese and Hindus. Mohammed permitted his devout followers to take four wives and as many concubines as they could support. As late as the nineteenth century, the Mormons founded a world-wide sect on the tenet that they had divine authority to propagate in multiple marriages.

Despite the dispensations to cohabit with plural wives, men obviously did not find spiritual or even sexual fulfillment in polygamy. When Kemal Atatürk abolished polygamy in the old Ottoman Empire after thirteen hundred years of endorsement by the Koran, he was opposed in the Moslem world by only a handful of feudal sheiks who maintained harems strictly as status symbols.

"If we inquire into the causes of polygamy, we meet with the surprising fact that purely sexual motives, such as desire for variety, preference for younger women, etc., were no more than subsidiary factors," Oswald Schwarz pointed out. "The decisive motives were social and economic. The number of his wives demonstrated the high social status or the wealth of a man. . . . Even among peoples where polygamy was practiced or not prohibited, it was by no means universal, but always restricted to the upper classes, a 'vicious luxury of the great.' "

Plutocrats and plebeians always have been lodge brothers, however, united by a male conceit that gave rise to the original justification for polygamy. The long periods of continence a woman can tolerate without distress is cited as proof that a man's innate sex drive is stronger and demands, therefore, more frequent releases of the pressures that build up in him. This is the old party line parroted by husbands to rationalize philandering, but there is absolutely no evidence to support it.

Most men isolated from feminine contacts by war or work quickly adjust to indefinite abstinence from sex with no adverse mental or physical effects. They do not climb the walls in frustration, lapse into depressions or suffer loss of vigor. Incessant references to sex are noisy rituals, like profanity and off-color stories, of the masculine mystique. The preoccupation with women in an all-male environment does not denote a craving for sex so much as a desire for the familiar pleasures of normal living conditions. Men are more obsessed with thoughts of appetizing food, liquor and tobacco when they are deprived of those creature comforts.

The male libido clearly fluctuates in direct relation to exposure to psychological stimulation, yet this explanation raises more questions than it resolves. Women are more alluring and accessible than ever before. Their forthright attitude toward sex is calculated to animate the erotic excitement that sustains the middle-aged man's potency. Then why are so many men past forty disturbed by sexual problems? Why are they trying desperately to boost their score in the numbers game or drifting into the apathy that is symptomatic of premature impotence?

The answers are found in the social forces that are ganging up on the middle-aged, middle-class man.

# 5

# Making a Living vs. Making a Life

\* \* \*

"A MARRIED MAN IS SEVEN YEARS OLDER IN HIS THOUGHTS the first day," Sir Francis Bacon noted dourly in 1606 when, at the age of forty-five, he reluctantly went to the altar with a wealthy merchant's daughter to get out of debt. It is a wry commentary on the human condition that Bacon, the father of modern philosophy, felt as trapped and timeworn by the pressures of society as the middle-aged man beset by money worries today.

Fear of financial insecurity has always exacted a heavier toll of the male's sexuality than any other factor except aging, but it holds special, private terrors for middle-class men who now are between forty and seventy. They are haunted by memories of the Depression, a traumatic experience that left an indelible scar on everyone who lived through it. Although they were not hit as cruelly as older people by the despair that racked the country, the threat of unemployment or downgrading in status still evokes a reminiscent shudder that clamps a vise on their libido.

A full generation has passed since the Depression, but it is astonishing how often references to it crop up in the conversation of older men and women. "We waited three years to get married during the Depression until Joe's salary was raised to thirty dollars a week. . . . People thought we were crazy to have a baby during the Depression. . . . I'll never forget the look on my father's face the day Roosevelt closed the banks. . . . My

73

seventeen-year-old son just asked for a raise in his allowance to ten dollars a week. That fed our entire family for a week during the Depression."

In gathering material for this book, some fifty medical authorities and sociologists were interviewed to discuss the forces shaping the middle-aged man's sexual attitudes. With few exceptions, they dwelled on the Depression at greater length— and with more personal involvement—than any other specific influence. Dr. Sophia J. Kleegman, a gynecologist and past president of the American Association of Marriage Counselors, smiled pensively when she was asked whether she saw increasing evidence of male sexual problems.

"I'm the last person in the world to ask that question," she replied. "It's difficult for me to draw a comparison between conditions today and twenty or thirty years ago, because my early experiences in counseling distorted, you might say, my viewpoint. I started working in the field in September, 1929. Six weeks later the stock market crashed. The catastrophic effect on healthy, virile men appalled me. I was like a young intern thrown into a cholera epidemic just after graduating from medical school. I got in one concentrated dose the worst crisis imaginable.

"The market crash was the most dramatic example ever seen of financial reverses affecting the male sex drive. Men who were worth fortunes on paper were wiped out, left penniless, overnight—in an hour. There was a grim joke among my older colleagues that the penises dropped faster than the stocks on Wall Street. We will never know how many men were made impotent temporarily by the crash. Six months later, it was routine to hear women say that they had had no sexual relations with their husbands since Black Thursday, the day the bottom fell out of the market.

"Every study of sex ever made has shown a high correlation between financial pressures and a reduction in the frequency of the male's desire for coitus. That is why there has always been more sexual activity in the upper and lower classes than in the middle economic group. The old saw that copulation is so popular among poor people because they have no other recreation is utter nonsense. The reason for the lower-class man's greater potency is that he lives so close to the margin of privation that the loss of income does not affect him as drastically as the middle-class man. I don't mean to sound callous, but it is a fact that the lower-class man today never had it so good, what with unemployment insurance and welfare benefits keeping him going in circumstances not much different from the conditions that are normal for him when he is working.

"The middle-class man lives on the brink of anxiety even when things are going well, for his major concern is consolidating his position on that income level. The loss of status immediately reduces his potency, because virility is equated with financial success in our society. A man caught up in the competitive rat race is so busy making a good living that he does not have the time or the energy to make a good life for himself."

Something more precious than money was lost during the Depression. Dr. Abram Jaffe, of Columbia University's Bureau of Applied Social Research, was discussing the undermining of masculine prestige by working wives, when he suddenly went off on an irrelevant tangent.

"The Depression had a curious psychological effect on me," he reflected. "I never have been able to save money since I was burned in the crash. It's a completely illogical frame of mind, I know, but I never have gotten over my distrust of banks. After graduating from high school in 1928, I went to work for two years to get enough money to enter college in September, 1930. I invested everything except my barest living expenses in the safest securities, bank bonds and mortgages, and I lost every dime in the crash. After that, I said the hell with scrimping to save money. It could disappear into thin air again or lose its value in an inflation.

"One of the few constructive results of the Depression was that thousands of college graduates of my era went into teaching. The shortage of teachers would be much more critical today if it were not for the influx of instructors, especially men, during the thirties. The salaries were miserable, but it gave us some measure of security which everyone was looking for desperately. At that, we were luckier than young doctors, lawyers and accountants who did not have money to set up private practice. They were forced to take Civil Service jobs at even worse salaries, which have continued to lag far behind the rest of the economy.

"The unprecedented prosperity since World War II has accentuated the bitterness and frustration of the Depression for those men. By the time the recession ended, they had family responsibilities which prevented them from quitting routine jobs beneath their capabilities and striking out into more challenging work. The Depression consigned them to a lifetime of mediocrity."

Veteran commentators drew upon the same bittersweet memories when the U.S. Census Bureau reported recently that nearly 60 percent of the country's population had not yet been born when the Depression began. Inez Robb, a columnist for the Scripps-Howard newspapers, wrote:

"To countless Americans—millions of us—who lived through the Depression, it is the single most searing experience of our lives. It was an endless time in which multitudes felt helplessly, hopelessly, adrift, with individual destiny beyond control.

"For us the Depression is automatically spelled with a capital D. I know men and women who have since achieved conspicuous success in their chosen fields whose only recurring nightmare is an icy-sweat terror in which they go from office to office, factory to factory, looking frantically for work that never materializes.

"The Depression remains so vividly alive for my generation

that it is almost impossible for us to grasp the fact that a succeeding generation has grown up to whom the Depression is as remote as the Revolutionary War or the Knights of the Round Table or the War of the Roses. It is now just another topic for a high school paper or a college thesis."

Miss Robb was not quite correct. The attitudes bred by the Depression have been the subject of serious study by large business corporations that maintain elaborate programs for the development and evaluation of top executives. Several years ago *Fortune* magazine made a survey of executives divided into three age groups: (1) older men who had launched their careers before the Depression, (2) middle-aged men who had commenced working during the Depression and (3) younger men whose business experiences had been confined to the postwar boom.

"The differences between the generations are crucial—not only in age, but in outlook, values and motivation," the survey concluded. The older men surprisingly were given the highest ratings for a sanguine view of business prospects. "Most of them came of age in a period of roaring prosperity which many thought would last forever. Then they experienced the long slide into depression followed by slow and painful recovery, war and then boom again. This succession of experiences has left them, above all, realists. Even at the nadir of the Depression they could foresee the possibility of a future boom."

The post-World War II generation had more modest salary goals than the two other groups and were more relaxed about their future security, principally because they "demonstrate a common inability to visualize a period of economic stress."

Middle-aged executives presented a disturbing picture. The Depression and then World War II, coming at the most impressionable stages of their careers, tended to make them conservative and "wary of booms." They also showed the highest incidence of anxiety and work-connected neuroses. Although the focus of the study was on professional performance, a personal problem was so apparent that a guarded reference was made to it: "In his sexual life the middle-aged executive frequently experiences the humiliation of a greater than average drop in sexual activity due to the exhausting demands of his job."

*Fortune* drew the same inference in a study of Bloomfield Hills, a suburb of Detroit described as "the densest concentration of working rich in the world." The wives of top executives and suppliers in the automobile industry hardly were enchanted with their marriages despite the material comforts they enjoyed. "My husband and I haven't been out together after nine o'clock at night for six months," a wife complained. "For all he gets out of it, we could be living in a cave."

A young clergyman in Bloomfield Hills said, "These men are monks—monks who have traded in their prayer books for a production line. From the way they work, I sometimes think they want to overwhelm God with their cars. It may sound odd for me to say this, but I don't give as much of myself to my church as many of them do to General Motors and Ford and the rest."

In a recent study of the personal lives of 8300 leading executives in the United States, sociologists W. Lloyd Warner and James C. Abriggen concluded that the group was not very active sexually. "Executives may be at the top of the ladder vocationally," a marriage counselor was quoted, "but they are at the foot when it comes to making love."

Those surveys, it should be noted, embraced men whose salaries averaged more than $25,000 a year. They owned their homes, were able to carry heavy insurance to protect their families, did not have to go into debt to educate their children and, in the great majority of cases, had guaranteed incomes after retirement. It has been established that people getting high monetary rewards can withstand stress better than those struggling to keep their heads above water. If stunted sex drives are a common condition in the upper echelon, how much worse is the situation among men in lower salary brackets?

Much worse, probably, than they are aware. Statistics on "normal" frequencies of intercourse at various age levels are misleading yardsticks of sexual potential, for the figures reflect *performance* rather than *capacity*. The fact that Kinsey found a marked decline in the male's rate of coitus after forty does not necessarily mean that a man must be resigned to sexual senescence after he passes that milestone.

"A man of fifty-five in good health is capable of having intercourse three times a week," Dr. William Ferber declares. "The trouble is that he takes his worries to bed with him. The brain is involved so intimately with sexual reactions that any sort of anxiety stifles the libido."

Admonishing a man to avoid pressures in order to enjoy a full, vigorous sex life is like telling the victim of a heart attack to forget his hospital and doctor bills and take things easy for three months. It is splendid advice, marvelous therapy, except for one drawback. The prescription does not provide a substitute for money. A man can give only so much of himself to his wife, family, friends, community and his work—and work is the last element to suffer when he must make a choice. The decision is inescapable, for the fulfillment of his other obligations is largely contingent on the energy he pours into his job and his recompense from it.

Making a good living honestly has never been easy, but there is no question that men in administrative positions are working harder today than ever before. The thirty-five- or forty-hour week—and some crafts are agitating for a twenty-five-hour week to maintain a high level of employment—is a hollow joke to men whose salaries, and responsibilities, are not fixed by union contracts. Paradoxically, the extension since World War II of such employee benefits as the five-day week, longer vacations and more holidays has increased sharply the daily work loads of management personnel, for they must accomplish much more in less time. The pressures are compounded by the mounting complexity of business brought by continual technological advances, new products and merchandising techniques, the proliferation of paper work and, above all, the maneuvering for promotions through the chains of command in big corporations, which, in absorbing smaller companies, have reduced the number of top-level jobs.

How hard do executives work? The question was investigated by the editors of *Fortune*, who reported their findings in *The Executive Life:*

"There is an interesting fiction these days that goes something like this: Executives are at last getting sensible about work. The worker long ago cut down his work week to forty hours or less and now the executive is doing the same. Why shouldn't he? Taxes, as top executives themselves so frequently say, have taken away the incentive to overwork. Furthermore, the argument goes, the trend to 'multiple management' makes the extra hours unnecessary anyway. Indeed, it makes them downright undesirable; since results come from many people working together in harmony, the effective executive is the rested man free from tensions, the man who prizes his leisure and encourages his subordinates to do the same.

"The facts? A study of executives' working habits—and executives' attitudes toward them—shows that:

"1. Executives are working as hard as they ever did. It is difficult to see how they could possibly work harder.

"2. Despite all grumbling by executives, high income taxes have had remarkably little effect on executives' drives.

"3. Executives are subject to more tensions than ever before. While the swing to 'human relations' and committee management has eliminated many of the old work pressures, it has substituted plenty of new ones."

Estimates of the average executive office week ran between forty-five and forty-eight hours—plus four nights of work a week away from the office. Home was described as "not a sanctuary so much as a branch office." The overall total for the week was a minimum of about sixty hours.

The grueling physical demands of a well-paying job are a heavy drain on a middle-aged man's energy for sexual activity, but the climate in which he works is even more debilitating. The shrill emphasis on youth throughout America has intensified enormously the anxieties of the middle-class man past forty, for age is the factor that largely determines employment and promotion opportunities. An employer considering a candidate for a job position once asked, "How good is he? What experience has he had?" The first question now is, "How old is he?"

Advances in medicine have added ten years to the male's life expectancy during the last generation, but the gain has been cancelled out by a corresponding shortening in his prime-of-life span on the labor market. It is axiomatic in large corporations that if a man has not made Executive Row by the time he is forty-five he never will. Each promotion is a calculated risk; the better the job, the less chance a man on the far side of forty has of getting a comparable position in the event he is displaced. The situation is no better among the rank and file. Until the 1950's, Help Wanted ads in newspapers occasionally specified forty-five as the cutoff age for applicants. Today, ads for white-collar workers are studded with the blunt warning, "Men over 35 need not apply."

Personnel managers have coined a word, "overqualified," to explain their rejection of competent middle-aged men in favor of younger candidates with lesser credentials. An "overqualified" man is too experienced for a job that will not "challenge" him or too mature to feel comfortable in a "shop with a young image." His background is too broad to work in narrow departmental channels or his talents will be demeaned by a job below the policy-making level and, unfortunately, the company filled just such a spot last month. In short, judgment and ability are handicaps. The interviews sound like scenes written by Kafka and played to the accompaniment of Gilbert and Sullivan's refrain from *H.M.S. Pinafore:*

"Things are seldom what they seem—
Skim milk masquerades as cream."

"The youth cult in business has been carried to ridiculous extremes," says Edwin Stern, the head of an executive placement agency in New York, "and I'm afraid it will get worse as the median age of the population continues to drop. It's twenty-seven now, and in another decade it will be down to twenty-five. I hate to think what will happen to the morale of people who have fifteen or twenty good years left and are thrown on the scrap heap. They will be the first fired and the last hired—a reversal of the seniority system that formerly gave employees a feeling of security and companies a sense of continuity."

Women supposedly are more sensitive than men about their age, but a number of sidelights underscore the male's preoccupation with presenting a youthful appearance. For example, women do most of the talking about dieting, but men watch calories more conscientiously because they have a more compelling motive. *Geriatrics,* a medical journal, made a nationwide study of obesity in 1963 and estimated that in the forty-to-seventy age group there were 12,693,000 overweight women compared to 8,324,000 men—a startling differential of more than 50 percent. Vanity prompts women to diet, but men do it through economic necessity. Slimness is associated with youth, a vital qualification for jobs.

The trend in men's fashions is another interesting case in point. Until fifteen years ago, the only style change in half a century had been the acceptance of sports clothes for informal wear. The sartorial model for young and mature businessmen was the solid, substantial image of the Wall Street banker—

broad-shouldered, double-breasted suit, thick gold chain across the waistcoat, square-rigged hat and squaretoed shoes denoting a citizen with both feet on the ground. Today, grandfathers affect the slim, tapering Ivy League look of Madison Avenue, which copied it from the understated casualness of the campus. The width of trousers, coat lapels, hat brims and even ties bought only five years ago seem outlandish now. The lines of everything a man wears are designed to create a slender, youthful silhouette.

Cosmetic products formerly beamed exclusively to women are gradually spreading to men's counters in drugstores. The Helene Curtis and Hazel Bishop companies recently announced they were working on a wrinkle-removing lotion for men. Clairol, the largest manufacturer of women's hair-coloring preparations, introduced in 1966 a home kit for men to cover up graying temples. Plush barber shops that specialize in disguising that first telltale of age are doing a brisk traffic at $15 a sitting.

"The only calls for dye jobs we used to get were from actors," the proprietor of a shop in midtown Manhattan says. "Now we're booked solidly by customers who come in twice a month for a touch-up around the temples. Practically all of them are businessmen in their early forties. There was a time young fellows were pleased when their hair started to turn gray. They thought it made them look mature and sort of distinguished. Now everybody wants to look like a college boy."

The pursuit of youth is a thoroughly natural drive—a far healthier reaction to aging than passive withdrawal from the mainstream of life. It stimulates intellectual curiosity in new ideas and active participation in the changing social scene that promotes a sense of vitality. If kept in proper perspective, the cultivation of youthful attitudes helps to quell the disquieting thought that time is running out on attainable goals. When competition with younger rivals becomes onerous, however, men from a background of sudden economic adversity may be assailed by self-doubts that produce a feeling of sexual inadequacy.

Men who were adolescents during the Depression and saw their fathers struggle futilely to maintain their economic status are particularly susceptible to what Dr. Abram Kardiner calls the "flight from the expectations of the masculine role." As Dr. Kardiner explains, "Money is the common form of vindication of manliness; by the same token, absence of money may crush the feeling of manliness."

Working wives also can have an emasculating effect on middle-aged men who witnessed the abdication of the masculine role to their mothers during the Depression. Stark necessity forced many wives to encroach on the male's prestige as the breadwinner of the family when their husbands were shut out of white-collar jobs by the lower wage scales for women. Until 1930, men outnumbered women in office jobs, but the great influx of female employees during the Depression reversed the ratio by a three-to-one margin.

A young son did not realize that his father, who had seemed so strong and resourceful, was helpless against the forces undermining his self-respect. He only knew that his mother was the dominant figure in the family, implanting in him doubts of his own ability to cope with the masculine role. Later in life, when confronted by a similar crisis, the boy grown older asks himself, "How can I stand up under the same pressures that beat down my father?"

Therapists familiar with the symptoms of impotence and related disorders in alumni of the Depression agree on the reason for the high percentage of patients who are married to career women. They believe that the men unconsciously chose wives who could share their financial burdens when they were young and struggling to gain footholds in their occupations. The partial surrender of masculine responsibilities did not disturb them when their sexual potency was high and newly married friends also were starting from scratch, but a drop in earning power in middle age while others are prospering arouses their fear of inadequacy as males.

Dr. Marie Nyswander treated George X, fifty-one, for melancholia after he lost his $20,000 job as the art director of an advertising agency that was absorbed by a larger firm. Originally a photographer more interested in camera techniques than administrative details, he had advanced by slow stages to the head of the department through seniority rather than ambition. As a young man he had been content to go along with the tide on the supplementary income earned by his wife Thelma, a school teacher. She had worked for ten years after the birth of their son until George's rising salary enabled her to retire.

Later, when Thelma discussed with Dr. Nyswander her marital relations, she recalled that George's libido had increased appreciably for a few years after she stopped working. "Judging from what I read in women's magazines, our intercourse had been just a little below the average for couples married our length of time," she said. "We slept together about once a week, usually on weekends, because I had to get up an hour earlier than George on school days. Sex had never been a big issue with George, so I was surprised, and flattered, when he began to make love to me occasionally during the week. He said he liked to see me in bed when he left for the office. Looking back, I suppose he meant he was proud that he no longer was dependent on my salary."

George was not unduly worried at first by the loss of his job. He was confident that the three months' severance pay he had been given would carry him until he made another connection. He went through the customary procedure of asking friends for leads to openings, sending his résumé to other agencies and answering ads in trade publications. During the first few weeks he received an encouraging number of replies with appointments for interviews. Several sessions seemed to go favorably until the question of salary came up and he mentioned the same figure he had made in his previous job. The curt tone of the discussions beyond that point was not lost on George. He cut his price to $17,500 at the next interview, but a young vice-president said the cost of bringing an employee of George's age into the company's pension plan would be prohibitive. When George said he was willing to forgo the pension, he was told that such waivers were not permitted by law.

As his prospects and bank balance evaporated, George began to lapse into long, sullen silences. Thelma, a sensible woman, had no illusions about the situation. At her insistence they gave up their car and moved from the East Side gold coast of New York to an apartment in a less fashionable neighborhood. George violently opposed another retrenchment, however, until he had no alternative. His son transferred from Dartmouth to New York University in the middle of the junior year to save the expense of living away from home.

In explaining to Dr. Nyswander why he resisted his son's transfer so strenuously, George used a peculiar phrase, which he applied to other emotional crises during that period. "I felt all shriveled inside that my son was being penalized for my failure as a father. I remembered what an awful letdown it was to me during the Depression when my father couldn't afford to send me to Princeton, his school." He smiled sardonically. "The only thing my father learned at Princeton was how to drink like a gentleman. No one except my mother knew that he was an alcoholic until he went to pieces during the Depression. I didn't even have that excuse when things got rough for me."

George's frustration after four months of unemployment exploded in a furious quarrel with Thelma when she told him that she was going back to work as a substitute teacher at $26 a day. Both were overwrought with pent-up anxieties and traded insults they later regretted. He accused her of making a sacrificial gesture to humiliate him. She retorted that someone had to pay the bills while he mooned around the house feeling sorry for himself.

The next morning George pocketed his pride and made the rounds of old contacts looking for assignments as a free-lance photographer. The manager of a news picture syndicate, who needed an expanded crew for President Lyndon B. Johnson's inauguration, hired him to cover the induction ceremony and the attendant social functions. The whole thing backfired badly. In the scrambling for good camera angles George was mauled and shoved out of range by younger rivals. That night he was so exhausted by his heavy equipment and the hand-to-hand competition at five inaugural galas that the syndicate used only one of the pictures he submitted.

After that fiasco George went into virtual seclusion. He stalked out of the room when Thelma or his son tried to draw him into conversation; he refused to see friends and former business associates. He tramped the streets collecting "mood" shots for an arty pictorial study of New York. No publisher was interested in the old chestnut, but George worked at it doggedly to keep up the pretext of being occupied with an important project. He did not ask Thelma how she managed to meet expenses on her salary.

"I knew she was borrowing money from her brother," he admitted to Dr. Nyswander, "but by that time I was too numb to feel ashamed. If anything, it was a relief to be going into debt instead of living off my wife like a kept man."

Thelma thought George would snap out of his depression when a résumé he had sent seven months earlier to a chain of department stores unexpectedly brought an offer of $13,000 a year to design layouts for its mail-order catalogue. She immediately stopped working in the hope of helping George regain his confidence, but he remained morose and uncommunicative. He brusquely cut off questions about his new job, dismissing it as "hack work any idiot with a paste pot and a pair of scissors can do." He had not slept with Thelma since she had gone back to work, but when she tried to make love to him to celebrate his first paycheck he turned away from her abruptly. She made another attempt a week later with the same result.

George's implacable hostility finally sent Thelma to Dr. Nyswander, who suggested a consultation with him. To Thelma's surprise, he agreed, after putting up a token resistance. Like many men torn by inner conflicts, he wanted to articulate and thrash out the doubts that were oppressing him. His reason for avoiding sexual relations with Thelma was a significant clue to his basic problem.

"I feel all shriveled inside," he said, the phrase that seemed to have a phallic connotation from him. "I can't act like a man in bed, because I know I'm a poor imitation of a man out of it."

He interpreted his setbacks—his failure to get a job comparable to the position he had lost, his inability to compete with younger photographers at the Inaugural, the slash in salary he had been forced to accept—as evidence of his waning virility. He resented Thelma's brief support of the family for exposing his inadequacy to his son, evoking guilty memories of the contempt he had felt for his own father during the Depression.

Healing the wounds to George's ego chiefly involved bringing him to the realization that every man must make realistic adjustments to conditions beyond his control. Dr. Nyswander showed him that, despite his self-condemnation, he had taken the most practical course in looking for a new job and had obtained one on his merits, without help from anyone. That it was not as good a job as he had hoped for was no reflection on his masculinity. Most men past fifty dislodged from a $20,000 job by a merger would have encountered the same difficulty in a highly specialized field.

Once George saw himself a typical middle-aged victim of the premium on youth in the labor market he began to rationalize his downgrading in status and became reconciled to it. Privately, he was relieved to be freed from the pressures of a job he never wanted, but a more important factor in his rehabilitation of his self-esteem was Thelma's initiative in making love to him. When Dr. Nyswander convinced him that Thelma had been motivated by sympathetic understanding rather than pity, his "shriveled" feeling of inadequacy gradually was dispelled.

Society gives short shrift to the Georges who have no consuming drive for success, yet relatively few men are spurred by vaulting ambition. There are three incentives that generate high singleness of purpose—the satisfaction of achievement, devotion to public service and the craving for the power of money or authority. But how many people possess the creativity that brings them a sense of fulfillment in work, sufficient dedication for the meager rewards of public service or the tenacity for the accumulation of power? The overwhelming majority are willing to settle for a place in the social scale one rung above the milieu in which they were reared.

It is standard procedure to denounce the gray conformity that is foisted on the Organization Man and stifles his individuality. A frightening picture is painted of Big Brother molding opinions and attitudes into rigid patterns as undistinguishable as soap wrappers rolling off an assembly line, but critics disregard the incontestable fact that most men value security above independence. Conformity is their refuge from making decisions that involve the risk of failure. A man may lose his identity in adopting the protective coloration of the herd, but there is safety in it.

The Organization Man is not a product of modern industry. He has been a stereotype throughout history, following the lead of bolder, more resourceful competitors. Several years ago Dr. Chris Argyris of Yale made a survey-in-depth on the attitudes of blue-collar workers and found that 77 percent did not aspire to positions of responsibility. We like to think that men on the management level are a more enterprising breed, but the ratio of those who are willing to gamble assured security for higher stakes is no greater than in the blue-collar group. More often than not, they are pushed out of comfortable niches into bigger jobs they must accept or betray themselves as unambitious time servers.

"Promotion neurosis" affects such men as severely as it does those who literally run themselves into the ground chasing the main chance. Psychosomatic ailments—palpitations, colitis, insomnia, asthma, arthritis—crop up so frequently among new arrivals on the upper echelons of large corporations that some staff physicians have concocted a placebo called "the executive pill" to relieve the anxieties of men who fear they have been thrust into jobs beyond their capabilities. By the time the physicians see them, however, many men have resorted to a common home remedy—the bottle. According to Selden Bacon, director of the Yale Center for Alcohol Studies, "Alcoholism becomes apparent after a ten- or twelve-year period of drinking development, usually between the ages of thirty-five and forty-five, when men of real promise are reaching a period of peak productivity and are at the point of assuming executive responsibility."

The urgency to make good quickly, the prevailing climate of business, saddles a man who is not overly aggressive with a sense of inferiority that gradually undermines his sexuality. He feels that he lacks virility for shrinking from the challenges in which competitors revel, that he is unworthy of his wife, because he is depriving her of social advantages. He feels alienated by a world moving so fast that he has no time to enjoy modest or even spectacular success. When John Schneider was lifted from obscurity to the presidency of the CBS-TV network in a startling shake-up on March 1, 1965, he unwittingly voiced a classic complaint. "I'm thirty-eight now, but I'll be fifty-five next week," he replied when he was asked what his first reaction was to the stunning promotion.

Some industrialists who have been in the thick of rugged competition for more than half a century are appalled by the pressures on young and middle-aged men today. When attention is focused on the high incidence of emotional crack-ups among executives, most management people point a defensive finger at other stresses—unhappy marriages, extravagant social climbing, personality defects—but a growing number of business leaders are discussing the problem candidly.

Shortly before Carl S. Hallauer, board chairman of the Bausch and Lomb Company, reached the mandatory retirement age of seventy in 1965, a magazine assigned me to write an article on his remarkable career in the American tradition of the self-made man. A destitute orphan at nine, he delivered newspapers from midnight to eight in the morning to support a younger sister, left high school after two years to heave coal at $8 a week and eventually rose to head the largest manufacturer of optical instruments in the country. The story was envisioned as an inspirational piece, but the idea was dropped. The magazine was afraid that advertisers would object to Hallauer's harsh appraisal of the current business scene.

While Hallauer was reminiscing about his early experiences, he walked from his rolltop desk to the glass partition in his office and gazed reflectively down Executive Row in the company's plant at Rochester, New York. "A fellow with my background will never sit here again," he said suddenly. "I'm like this desk, a throwback to another era. Business is so complex now and changes so fast that it's impossible for a kid to break in at the bottom and gradually work up to the top as I did. The Horatio Alger heroes of my generation would be lost in the shuffle trying to keep up with these high-powered boys."

He nodded toward the adjoining offices visible through the partition. Next door the number-two man, President William McQuilken, was a former Rhodes scholar from Princeton.

Graduates of the Naval Academy, Dartmouth, Yale and Caltech followed in the chain of command.

"Every big company has a comparable line-up of talent," Hallauer went on. "There's no question that management is more competent than it was years ago, but we're paying an awfully stiff price for efficiency in terms of people. Fellows bucking for promotion have to keep punching and driving themselves so hard that they can't stop to smell the flowers and enjoy the scenery along the way. I'm glad that I'm not going through the wringer now. It squeezes all the juices out of men. You should talk to Harry Hagerty. He's seen more men under business pressures than anybody in America."

Harry Hagerty, another old Rochester boy, went to work on a road gang at sixteen and wound up vice-president in charge of investments for the Metropolitan Life Insurance Company, the largest private lending agency in the world. Until his mandatory retirement in 1962, Hagerty made the final judgment on commercial loans averaging $1,500,000,-000 annually for projects ranging from rural pipe lines to atomic energy plants.

"It seems to me that there's a feeling of desperation in men working for large corporations, as though their futures depend on every move they make," Hagerty said. "The exaggerated accent on youth in this country has created a timetable for success that leaves no margin for error or even a slight delay in advancement. At thirty-five, a man must be firmly established as a comer who has shown superior qualifications for a big job. At forty-five, he must be in a position to make a decisive jump all the way to the top. If he has not gotten there at fifty, the chances are he never will. Beyond that point he is running in quicksand while younger men are burning up the track.

"This continual weeding-out process is supposed to open up opportunities for good people down the line, but the system benefits no one. Employees who are by-passed early in their careers stop trying to catch up with the parade or they become bitter with frustration. The men who do survive the elimination contests are loaded with such heavy responsibilities during the relatively few years they are in charge of operations that they have no time to develop mature, long-range perspectives."

He pondered for a long moment. "They say youth must be served. Whatever became of wisdom and experience?"

# 6

# The Climacteric

***

THE KEY TO AN ACTIVE AND HEALTHY SEX LIFE AFTER FORTY
is so simple that it seems a man should be able to sustain his
potency indefinitely with the same sensible adjustments he
makes to the slowdown of his other physical functions. It
merely involves living within his economic and emotional
means, but the catch with Golden Rules is that they call for
more patience and mature judgment than most people are
capable of exercising under the stresses of the Affluent Society.

There are two types of intangible forces that tend to blunt a
middle-aged man's libido. One is anxiety, a by-product of the
great American pastime of keeping upset with the Joneses.
The other antedates the Old Testament's lamentations for the
lost vigor of youth. Somewhere between the ages of forty-five
and fifty-five, every man goes through the climacteric, a period
that corresponds to a woman's emotional turmoil during the
menopause.

In many men the climacteric is just a vague feeling of discontent or futility that passes after a few months. Others view
their prospects through the dark glasses of discouragement for
a year or so and are apt to fly into sudden, irrational fits of
anger. In a small, but significant, percentage of cases the
climacteric is marked by severe melancholia that requires
psychiatric treatment. Curiously enough, men in the latter
group often are on the verge of attaining long-coveted objectives or are about to tackle the most important projects of

their careers when they are demoralized by an overwhelming, inexplicable fear of failure.

It should be emphasized that the climacteric is a temporary phase with no adverse effects on the majority of men. There may be some disturbing changes in habits and attitudes, but such symptoms invariably disappear if there are no serious ruptures in a man's personal relationships while he is riding out the squall. But that can be a big if, for he is liable to alienate his family, friends and business associates with rash outbursts not unlike the tirades of a neurotic, peevish woman.

Hitherto even-tempered men have been known to jeopardize good, hard-to-duplicate jobs by provoking violent arguments with their employers. It is no coincidence that the divorce rate, which begins to drop steadily after the fourth year of marriage, rises sharply again with the onset of the climacteric. Sexual problems, particularly premature impotence, often can be traced to the pattern of sporadic intercourse dispirited men fall into while they are struggling through the climacteric.

In a sense, the climacteric is like a nuclear explosion in that the fallout may be more damaging than the immediate blast. As Dr. Kenneth Walker points out: "Psychologists trace the beginnings of our adult problems to our tenderer years and in consequence of this they place great stress on the upbringing of children. Little has as yet been said about the influence our middle years exert on the decades that follow them. . . . What we have sown in our earlier years we later reap, and this is as true of the physical disabilities of old age as it is of the psychological troubles."

The climacteric, therefore, is the critical prelude to the twenty or thirty remaining years in a man's life span. It is a period of transition—an adolescence in reverse. The adolescent is impatient to grow up and enjoy the freedom and privileges of maturity. The man passing the crest of middle age wants to stop the clock and cling to his potency and peak productivity.

Since the libido is the primary expression of the life force, he subconsciously measures the success or failure of his fight to resist senescence by his sexual activity. That is why it is essential for husbands—and wives—to make special efforts to maintain regular, frequent marital relations during the climacteric and to stimulate their love-making with new erotic techniques.

The cause of psychological impotence was spelled out by Dr. Oswald Schwarz: "The answer is the same as in any other case of sexual difficulties: a deficient sense of virility. In a fairly large group of cases this is due to the tension between the gradually decreasing vitality and the still heavy demands on a man's energy. The difference produces a definite sense of growing inadequacy, and as sexuality is very sensitive to even a slight disturbance of our psychological budget it is only to be expected that the sexual capacities of these men suffer first and most.

"A second reason is that sexuality more and more loses its importance as men grow older and occupational worries take its place. But as sexuality is, apparently, very sensitive to such a loss of prestige, it withdraws if it is no longer wholeheartedly wanted. This motive is the cause why in many marriages sexual relations between husband and wife cease during these critical years. It is not that through habit and the familiarity of many years of married life the wife loses attraction for her husband; we know by now that these things do not exist. The real cause is that the marriage has ceased to be a living union, and that other interests, pleasant and unpleasant, have become dominant; not the physical potency of the man is dying but the incentive to employ it."

Until a few years ago the climacteric was a highly controversial issue in medical circles. The majority rejected the idea that a man goes through a phase similar to a woman's menopause, arguing that there was no evidence of a dramatic "change of life" such as the female's cessation of ovulation and a reduction in her supply of sex hormones. Endocrinology was an infant science, and few psychologists had investigated the phenomena of aging.

Some studies of the climacteric had been made, notably by Dr. Gregorio Marañón, a Spanish pathologist. In 1929 he observed that emotional instability was a frequent characteristic of middle-aged men and was manifested by such reactions as irritability, crying spells, conversion to religion, inability to concentrate and a sense of being ill-used by society. Marañón offered little documentation of his findings, however, and his work was flawed—for prosaic authorities—by fanciful flights of Latin romanticism. "A man's heart does not acquire full capacity for love and for every delicate or passionate sentiment until between the fortieth and fiftieth years," he rhapsodized. "Then man is more seductive than at any other time." Since Marañón himself was forty-two and squarely in the decade of maximum seductiveness, colleagues who had not yet reached it callously rejected his premise as wishful thinking.

Hardly any new material on the male climacteric appeared until *The Journal of the American Medical Association* published in 1939 a paper by Dr. August A. Werner, of the St. Louis University School of Medicine. Werner corroborated the personality changes mentioned by Marañón and added a number of physical factors, including loss of potency and an imbalance of sex hormones. The article aroused little comment, but six years later professional opinion was divided sharply when Werner presented an elaborate statistical compilation comparing the disorders of women during the menopause with those of middle-aged men who had admitted a reduction in sexual activity.

Werner listed some thirty-five complaints and reported only minor differences between the ratio of men and women who suffered from such ailments as nervousness, depression, insomnia, crying, headaches and hypochondria. "Probably a greater number of men than of women pass through the climacteric without any evident disturbance," he declared. "However, this inference may be based on the fact that knowledge of the occurrence of this syndrome in man is of very recent date and that the condition possibly has been overlooked or ignored."

Critics challenged Werner's statistics, insisting that it was impossible to measure with any degree of accuracy the subjective feelings he had catalogued. They asserted that a college freshman boning up for exams could very well have the same symptoms. The people in the control group also were viewed with suspicion. "One man worried and cried while at work," Werner wrote, "because he thought that his wife smoked cigarettes while he was away." Skeptics dismissed such subjects as neurotic nuts.

Today, those debates over the climacteric seem as absurd as the objections of medieval doctors to ventilated bedrooms lest sleepers were exposed to a miasma in the night air. With the exception of a few die-hards, medical authorities now agree that the male climacteric, although essentially a psychological conflict, is no less real than the female menopause, which has a biological substructure. In 1953 the American Psychiatric Association published a manual declaring that disorders originating in the mind of middle-aged men were "characterized by depressions or paranoid ideas manifested by worry, insomnia, guilt, anxiety, agitation, delusional ideas and somatic (physical) concerns." It warned that men with severe symptoms were suicidal risks.

Self-pity, the easiest emotion, is a prevalent reaction to the climacteric in mild as well as acute cases. Many men, worried by their diminishing rate of sexual intercourse, cushion the blow to their self-esteem by attributing the loss of libido to poor health. They complain of fatigue and vague aches and pains, diagnosing every new twinge as the first stage of a morbid disease. Men who live and work in a compatible atmosphere usually snap out of their depressions quickly, but those who meet with unrelieved discouragement begin to lean heavier on infirmities as a crutch to their pride and eventually turn into full-fledged hypochondriacs.

"Man's best possession is a sympathetic wife," Euripides said 2500 years ago. A complication of the climacteric is that it often coincides with the menopause of a wife who is several years younger than her husband. He may feel miserable and need a good deal of understanding himself, but he cannot extort it with tears and tantrums. That is a woman's exclusive prerogative. He must suffer in silence—and, perhaps, in ignorance. The female is taught from puberty to expect the menopause, but the male's sexual education is such a conglomeration of half-truths picked up at random that he does not know what is happening to him when his private world goes to pieces. At a time when it is vital for him to reaffirm his masculinity his wife may be plagued by doubts of her desirability, with the result that neither provides the assurance the other wants so desperately.

The overall factor that makes the climacteric a more difficult period for some men than others is the individual's capacity to absorb stress, to roll with the punches and disappointments that befall everyone at any age. The first target attacked by any sort of disagreeable tension, Dr. Hans Selye discovered, is the libido. The sex glands shrink, and there is a drastic reduction in the male's sperm cells. In women, the menstrual cycle becomes irregular or stops.

It should be noted that specific reference was made to disagreeable tension, for not all stress is unpleasant or undesirable. The excitement of a big social event, a sports contest, a new experience, a reunion after a long separation, the impending fulfillment of an ambition is accompanied by a feeling of nervous exhilaration. A veteran actor may be paralyzed by stage fright before the curtain rises, but he revels in the anticipation of facing the audience. An athlete is worried if he does not have butterflies in the pit of his stomach just before he goes into action; the sensation primes him for his initial explosion of energy. And then there is the exquisite tension that infuses every part of the body before an orgasm.

Stress is harmful only when it is not relieved. Actually, brief spells of tension are beneficial for flushing out the torpor that can clog the nervous system like rust in a machine; nothing is more debilitating than too much rest or lack of mental stimulation. A sexual relationship without occasional emotional flare-ups is as flat as living in a vacuum with a somnambulist.

"The reason that the course of true love never does run smoothly is the fact that true love can endure only if the provocations of anger and resentment which inevitably develop are freely expressed and discussed and readjusted to," Dr. Karl Menninger said. "I certainly do not mean wrangling; both parties must make some conscientious effort to achieve objectivity and not simply indulge in temper tantrums. . . .

"It always seemed to me significant that among the Jews, where there is such a noticeable tendency to express aggressions in argument and verbal combat, there are so few divorces and so little physical violence. It is my idea that, even if the Roman Catholic church did not forbid it, divorce would still be infrequent among the Irish and Italians, because of their relatively great facility in expressing their emotions. It is often assumed by the silent, dignified, sulky Anglo-Saxon that the avoidance of verbal or even physical conflict between husband and wife promotes peace and happiness.

"The story of the European peasant woman who wept because her husband had not beaten her for a month seems grotesquely and pathetically amusing, but it is psychologically true. If a woman has to choose between being ignored and being beaten she will certainly choose the latter. Although this might be construed as a recommendation of wife-beating, that is certainly not what I mean; I do mean that if hostilities cannot be repressed or diverted, it is better to have them *out* than to have them *in*."

Every layman knows that the greater tensions to which men are subjected are the principal reason why they die younger than women and also accounts for the greater number of male patients in mental institutions. Dr. Henry I. Russek, a consultant at the U.S. Public Health Hospital on Staten Island, New York, summed up a recent study of one hundred men less than forty-five years old who had suffered coronary heart attacks: "Emotional stress of occupational origin may be far more significant in the etiologic (causative) picture of coronary disease than heredity, dietary fat, tobacco, obesity or physical activity."

The effect of stress on human sexuality has not yet been investigated as thoroughly as it should be, but some valuable deductions can be drawn from studies of animals. Most people will be surprised to learn that the crude sex drive of animals in captivity or a natural state is appreciably lower than man's. Among other mammals, copulation is limited to the infrequent periods when the female is in heat, but men and women are sexually responsive at all times. Since man is the highest, most complex, mammal, it is logical to assume that pressures which disrupt an animal's mating habits also will influence his sexual behavior in some degree.

For example, an increase in a zoo's population, producing conditions comparable to urban congestion and a heightening of group pressures, invariably is accompanied by a sharp decrease in the animals' potency. The opposite result might be expected, for wild animals' nervous energy is expended mainly in searching for food and protecting themselves against attack. These basic needs are provided in captivity, but crowding and frustration more than counteract the measures for the animals' health and safety.

In 1935 the Philadelphia Zoo, the oldest in the United States, was the first one in the world to put animals on a balanced diet. The death rate quickly dropped 25 percent, the longevity of the animals jumped the equivalent of five years in the human life span, and there was more mating activity. At the same time, however, there was a steady decline for a decade in the number of animals on display. During the Depression the Zoo's appropriations were slashed, and then World War II halted the importation of new specimens from Asia and Africa. A few years after the pens and cages had been restocked, the death rate was hitting an all-time high and some species had stopped breeding.

"The animals are bigger and stronger, but there are fewer outlets for their vigor," explained Dr. Herbert Ratcliffe, of the University of Pennsylvania School of Medicine, and director of the Zoo's research laboratory. "We must conclude that unrelieved tensions are shooting up the death rate. Worse yet, the incidence of arteriosclerosis, also a leading cause of death in man, is ten times higher than it was in 1935. All this ties in perfectly with studies in the density of human population.

"One of our camels, a five-year-old female, died from a peptic ulcer, which is practically unheard of in a ruminant. We had her in a small enclosure with her brother and sister. Camels at best are nasty beasts. I think our victim died from the sheer aggravation of having to look at other camels incessantly. By the same token, a disgruntled person thrown into close contact with other people may become a misanthrope and eat himself up with irritation."

Another interesting comparison of tensions in the animal kingdom was made by Dr. Mark W. Allam, dean of the University of Pennsylvania School of Veterinary Medicine, in a paper dealing with the rapid recovery of animals after major operations that incapacitate people for long periods. Dogs usually are walking, eating and drinking six hours after surgery, and a horse is up and about within a day. Conceding that animals are less sensitive to pain than man, Allam ventured the opinion that they recuperate faster, because they are not concerned with doctor bills, hospital expenses and time lost from a job—worries that delay human convalescence.

Millions of Americans, now middle-aged, who heard shots fired in anger during World War II need no evidence other than their own experiences for proof of the impact of persistent stress on the libido. A license to brag of his amatory triumphs overseas was issued with every serviceman's discharge papers, but there is one infallible test for separating fact from fantasy. If he tells of besieging a romantic objective when he was in imminent danger of enemy attack, he is tearing the tissue of the truth into confetti. Sex ranked approximately twentieth on a combat soldier's list of urgent desires. The first half were to get out of the flicking war alive. The next half-dozen were to get out of the flicking uniform. Sex was a distant also-ran behind a furlough, good chow and a bed with clean sheets.

The National Research Council enlisted two hundred psychiatrists in 1955 for a follow-up study of the predominant neuroses and gripes in all branches of the armed forces during the war. "Only 3 percent of the servicemen suffering from inherent military and environmental stress [boredom, fear, discipline, loss of privacy] complained about the lack of sexual outlets," they concluded. "None mentioned anything related to sex in reporting specific forms of combat stress."

Max Zera, an infantry captain who later was the public relations officer of the First Division, which spearheaded the invasions of North Africa, Sicily and Normandy, was asked to comment on the survey. "There's no question that combat drove all thoughts of sex out of the G.I.'s minds," he said. "While we were training in the States there was a lot of tomcatting and shacking up with local talent, but all that stopped after our first fire fight in North Africa. There were several brothels in Oran supervised by the Army to control venereal disease, but the few guys who went to them did it strictly out of curiosity. Most of the time they didn't go upstairs with the girls. They drank a couple of bottles of beer, kidded the girls who understood English and went back to camp.

"The longer we were in the line, the less interest there was in sex. After we were pulled out of Sicily and shipped to England to get ready for the invasion of Europe, the G.I.'s gradually began to loosen up again. We were in England seven months, and the girls were very cooperative, but few married men played around as much as they had in the States. It was my impression that they felt guiltier about their infidelity. Although the guys in combat units tried to rationalize it on the grounds that the odds were against their survival, they never quite convinced themselves that they were justified in letting down the moral bars.

"Many single fellows had the same sense of guilt. They became formally engaged to girls with whom they were having affairs and would have married them if the Army had permitted it. The top brass knew our casualties would be heavy, and they didn't want to burden the British with young widows. After the war, a surprising number of G.I.'s went back to England and married girls who had slept with them."

A similar reaction was prevalent among bomber crews, despite the strange nature of the war they fought in Europe. Ground troops called it a "country club" war. In the morning, the Flying Fortresses were dodging flak and clobbering targets in Germany. The same evening, the crews were living it up in towns adjacent to their British bases—until they had flown three or four missions. Shortly after launching operations in England, the Eighth Air Force revised its policy of giving combat men extended furloughs in London and set up military rest homes in isolated areas. It found that the men were bored and drifted aimlessly when they were on their own in a big city. Many returned to the base before their leaves were up, resentful of civilians who were not exposed to their danger.

If there was one aphrodisiac calculated to stimulate a young G.I.'s gonads, it was Paris, but a blitzkrieg on its commercial pleasures did not come until they were far behind the battle lines. According to some accounts, Paris was an orgastic spree for American troops who liberated it on August 25, 1944. *Time* magazine painted a purple picture of jeeps parked outside apartment houses all night and tousled girls climbing out of tanks on the Champs Elysées the following morning. It neglected to mention that the vehicles were attached to the Second French Armored Division, which had seen practically no action and was appointed to lead the task force into the undefended city as a gesture to boost civilian morale.

The French girls who gave a delirious welcome to everyone in an American uniform were not exactly rebuffed, but there was, under the circumstances, remarkably little consummation of hands-across-the-sea rapport in bed. At about seven o'clock the evening after the liberation I met Don Whitehead, the front-line war correspondent for the Associated Press, in the lobby of the Hôtel Scribe, Allied press headquarters. I had been hoarding a bottle of Scotch since the Normandy beachhead for a suitable occasion, and we went up to my room to celebrate the best one in sight.

It had been a jewel of a summer day, and now Paris shimmered in a golden haze burnished by the setting sun, and the air smelled as though a thousand girls wearing a wonderful perfume had just passed. A long sigh of relief seemed to envelop the city; even the trigger-happy F.F.I. resistance fighters had stopped firing at suspected German collaborators hiding out on rooftops.

Whitehead turned from the window and shook his head. "I'll bet you and I are the only Americans in Paris who aren't getting laid," he said. "I realized today I'm getting too old for this war [he was thirty-six] when I looked at all the fancy fluff on the loose and my only thought was that it was too damn much trouble to climb into the sack and have a go at it. Come on, pappy. Let's get some chow and cackle about the devilish times we had on Saturday nights necking in the balcony of the Bijou."

Feeling as forlorn as waifs on Christmas, we headed for the

Army mess in the basement of the hotel, but we never reached it. The bar en route was mobbed as though travel orders to the States were being issued to all comers. Officers, enlisted men and correspondents, drawn together by the excitement of the last two days, were swapping experiences, second-guessing the generals and debating how much longer the war would last. There wasn't a female in the place, although a convention of streetwalkers and budding apprentices had been in session in front of the hotel all day.

Two M.P.'s who were patrolling the streets came in at midnight and said the prostitutes had stopped soliciting G.I.'s to look for more promising customers. Within a few days the girls were approaching men in uniform mainly to cadge cigarettes, and that's how it was until the rear-echelon commandos moved in and enriched the hustlers and the clip joints in Montmartre beyond the dreams of avarice.

It is just as well for Dr. D. W. Heyder and Helen Wambach, a psychologist, that a paper they wrote in 1964, "Sexuality and the Effect on Frogmen," was buried in *Archives of General Psychiatry*. They would have been denounced as subversives by the American Legion, D.A.R. and other flag-waving organizations if their findings had been circulated in the newspapers. The purpose of their survey was to study the effects of severe, prolonged emotional and physical stress on volunteers for the Navy's frogman training program at Norfolk, Virginia. Through the years the average dropout rate had been about 75 percent—an abnormally high figure that indicated better methods were needed to screen candidates for the tough course.

Interviews with men who quit after a week or two uncovered one strong clue. Most of them gave variations on the same reasons: "My wife wanted me to stop" or "I got lonesome for my girl." In their summary the authors declared, "The group that completed frogman training apparently had fear of women and doubts of their own sexual adequacy. It is, of course, only a speculation, but it is quite possible that their unconscious motivation to complete the course was based on a need to prove their masculinity, coupled with the fear of involvement with women."

General George C. Marshall described war as long stretches of boredom punctuated by spasms of intense fear. Substitute discontent for fear, and the statement summarizes a man's mood during the climacteric. He is at war with himself; like Hamlet, he must flog his will to make it obey his instincts. Sex, having lost its biological incentive for reproduction, seems "weary, stale, flat and unprofitable," but he continues to play the numbers game, because his social conditioning has established it as an index to his virility. He would like to renounce the social pressures that are compelling him to run faster on the treadmill to keep up with the competition, but his conscience and pride will not permit him to shirk his family obligations. He grouses that he is getting no fun out of life going through the same old social routine with the same people, but he is hard-pressed for an answer when he is asked what diversions would hold more zest for him.

The years immediately before and after a man's fiftieth birthday are a difficult period under the most favorable circumstances. It is a time for taking stock of himself and, more often than not, the inventory is disappointing. In his youth a man wonders where he is going. In middle age he still does not know his final destination, but he already is three-quarters of the way there—and time is running out on his ambitions.

Only a clod with mediocre standards ever is completely satisfied with his accomplishments. After Babe Ruth had retired from baseball with the unapproachable record of 714 home runs, he was asked whether he looked back on his career with any regrets.

"Sure," he boomed. "I wish I'd hit seven hundred and fifteen homers."

The gulf between aspirations and reality often is magnified

in middle age by a man's nagging suspicion that he has pursued the wrong goal. A career planned in the twenties may assume an entirely different perspective a quarter-century later; the view from the top often is less exciting than the visions that spurred the climb. One of the elite groups in American industry is comprised of executives chosen by the Alfred P. Sloan Foundation to study at M.I.T. the theory and practice of management decisions. There are two separate divisions: the Sloan Fellows, who average thirty-six years old and take a year's course leading to a master's degree, and the Senior Executives, who are in their middle forties and are put through a ten-week program. The men in both divisions are assured of promotion in their companies and handsome material rewards, but some years ago a faculty member noted a significant difference in their attitudes.

"The Sloan Fellows just know that they are going up and will get there," he observed. "The Senior Executives wonder whether their efforts are worth making. Their questioning isn't questioning of the system—although they got the full shock of the Depression—but rather of a moral, ethical and philosophical kind. Their concern is how it all fits together."

As a man approaches fifty, the shape of things to come does not interest him as vitally as his place in it. In moments of self-doubt he morosely wonders whether he is turning into an old fogy and becomes increasingly sensitive to intimations of his conservatism or stodginess. He bridles when he is told, "Things are done differently than they were years ago" or "You don't understand what's happening in the world." The truth of the matter is that he cannot fathom a great many things that are changing the world he knew.

A maxim attributed to Anatole France sums up an individual's psychological orientation to his environment: "If a man is not a radical at twenty, there is something wrong with his heart. If he still is a radical at sixty, there is something wrong with his head." The older a man gets, the stronger he resists new concepts and customs. He is perfectly capable of adjusting to changing conditions, but he clings to the past to identify with a more vibrant period in his life.

He tells anecdotes to illustrate what a dashing, resourceful fellow he was, and the farther the incidents recede into his background the more vivid they are to him. He is alternately offended and baffled by the impatient, and stupefied, looks of young people at stories that are fascinating to him. He does not realize that half the population of the United States was not yet born at the outbreak of World War II and that his captive audience never heard of most of the personalities who made headlines a generation ago.

It is a curious fact that college, fraternal and military reunions are attended by larger contingents of men in their fifties than any other age group. One might assume that death, illness and outdated mailing lists would cut down the turnout of the older boys, but they are drawn by something more personal than sentimental attachment to the school or the organization. They want to see themselves through the eyes and the reminiscences of acquaintances who knew them when they were young and ebullient.

The one area in which a middle-aged man can demonstrate that he is able to function with unimpaired competence is in his work. As we have seen, he may try subconsciously to compensate for his declining rate of sexual intercourse by making his job the principal focus of his interest and energy. Another occupational variation of the numbers game creates a common, although misunderstood, problem in large companies. An executive who feels impelled to prove he is as good a man as ever will suddenly increase his work load by assuming tasks he previously delegated to subordinates—a bid for approval that invariably results in the opposite impression.

Indecision, a component of fatigue, begins to hamstring his efficiency as details clutter his mind and his desk. Despite the mounting backlog of work, he stews over routine chores on the pretext of checking up on mistakes that may slip through other departments. He likes to think he is the stickler for accuracy the company needs to keep less responsible boys on the ball, but his delays are a form of psychic featherbedding—evasions to prolong the job at hand and defer the burdens of subsequent assignments. Instead of expediting matters he is a bottleneck in the organization, and when his superiors tactfully advise him to ease up and give his staff more latitude he flies into a panic suspecting they are grooming a younger man to supplant him.

This vicious circle of self-imposed pressures compounding false fears is a standard pattern in middle-aged men who suddenly are oppressed by a feeling of sexual inadequacy. It generally begins with an apathetic session of love-making following an exhausting period of concentration on work, causing a man to wonder whether he is losing his desire for coitus. Apprehensive of another poor performance in bed, he further disrupts his normal cycle of intercourse to prime himself for a good, strong orgasm, but he is so tense and preoccupied with his response during foreplay that he rushes through it to a weak or a premature ejaculation.

Now he is caught in a self-perpetuating bind. His shaken self-confidence intensifies his doubts, which in turn build up a series of blocks to his libido. Since he always has associated sex with youthful vigor, he glumly assumes he indeed must be an old fogy if he has no zest for the pleasures of the matrimonial—or any other—bed. He feels alienated from the dynamic tempo of his milieu and retreats into a shell of indifference to sex to forestall further blows to his ego.

Actually, the great majority of men in their fifties today are better attuned to their environment than their counterparts in any modern era. The impact of the 1920's on people who had been born a half-century earlier certainly was more bewildering than the changes in mores witnessed by the present middle-aged generation since it reached maturity. Some aspects of the current sexual climate may disturb parents of adolescents, but the situation hardly is as shocking as their own wholesale scrapping of Victorian conventions after World War I. Men who were indoctrinated to the New Deal during the Depression are as progressive, politically and socially, as first voters. They grew up with the automobile, the airplane, movies and the radio, which broke down the barriers of provincialism and exposed them to a wider variety of people, places, experiences and ideas than their fathers ever knew.

The slang of the jazz era, the primary source of idioms for hepcats and cool cats, jivesters and hippies, has enabled them to keep up with new patterns of speech. The songs by Gershwin, Rodgers, Porter, Berlin and Kern that were played at their school dances still are heard constantly. They cut their intellectual eyeteeth on the realism that has been the dominant trend in literature for the last four decades. They were caught up from the beginning, as participants and spectators, in the sports craze of the twenties that revamped the nation's leisure habits.

Paradoxically, the middle-aged, middle-class man often paints himself into a corner trying too hard to be With the Scene. Two decades of unprecedented prosperity since World War II have brought sweeping changes in the concept of conspicuous consumption. A man's social standing once was manifested chiefly by his home and its furnishings, his car, his wife's fine feathers and the servants he employed. With the exception of the servants, his status symbols were material possessions with a certain durability. A three-year-old Cadillac had more cachet than a new Ford or Chevrolet, a redecorated living room was a conversation piece for months, and a lot of mileage could be gotten from a new fur coat.

Today, the wage earner in a medium bracket is spending an increasing proportion of his salary on the peripheral trimmings of the Affluent Society to maintain a facade instead of shoring up a secure financial foundation of his position. The big difference lies in recurring expenses for services as distinguished from outright purchases of goods that have tangible value. In 1946, his expenditures for services were one-third of his income. In 1967, they accounted for almost 45 percent.

A two-week vacation at a nearby resort makes him look like a second-class citizen when everyone, or so it seems, is going to Europe and taking winter holidays in Hawaii and the Caribbean. What was In last month is old hat this week; expensive, superficial fads rather than discriminating tastes are the measures of sophistication. The culture of mid-century America requires him to provide his children with advantages, private schools, organized recreation, cars, only the wealthy could afford when he was young.

"A middle-aged man straining to keep up appearances eventually resents the demands made on him," reports Mrs. Minna Holtzberg, associate director of a recent survey of marital problems made by the Family Service Association of America. "Everyone is saying 'more, more' to him—his employer, his wife, his children. A man has just so much psychic energy, and when he reaches the limit of it he rebels against further impositions on him.

"He rarely protests openly by taking such drastic steps as leaving his family or quitting a job that has become intolerable. The immediate target of his accumulated anger invariably is his wife. He strikes back at her by withholding himself sexually from her. 'I may have to support you, but I won't give you anything in bed,' he says subconsciously. 'There are other women who will appreciate me more than you do.'

"Despite his feeling of hostility, we have found that a man who is brooding over financial pressures at home does not deliberately set out to have an affair to punish his wife. If he does get involved in an extramarital episode, he generally drifts into it with a woman he has known for some time through his work. As a rule, she is a divorcee or an unmarried woman past thirty who is starved for exactly the same things he is—a little attention and affection. That's all she wants from him, and it is such a relief from him to get away from the demands of his family that he actually would be satisfied to have a platonic relationship with her.

"There is more pathos than passion in most of these affairs. She invites him to dinner in her apartment, he brings a bottle of wine, and they go through the sexual by-play each expects of the other when a mature man and woman are in an intimate situation. They go to bed, not because they are infatuated, but simply to lean on a sympathetic shoulder for a few hours.

"It's tragic what a tremendous difference a few considerate words would mean to a man who feels that his wife and children regard him as a money machine. Our culture expects a middle-class father to give his children college educations, but no one asks whether he can afford it. The kids assume that Dad will send them to any school that will accept them and, with the rare exceptions of men who are embittered by their own failures, good old Dad knocks himself out to come through like clockwork with checks for tuition and allowances.

"Bank loans to defray the cost of college now are as common as mortgages to buy houses, and small wonder. The U.S. Office of Education recently estimated the expenses for four years in a state college add up to about $9000 and in a private institution to $16,000. In another decade the cost will double. The average middle-aged man who puts two children through college has to abandon any thought he might have had of retiring. He still will be paying off the loans in ten years, and if a son goes on to graduate school he will be in debt even longer. Lord knows how many men have given up smoking and bring their lunch to work in dispatch cases to save a few dollars a week so that they can keep their children in school.

"That's not the full extent of their sacrifices. It is taken for granted that they will support children who get married while still in school and that the allowances will be increased if the young couples have babies. Our files are crammed with cases of men who are in such a constant turmoil over money that they stop having marital relations with their wives.

"The father of a college sophomore who eloped with a girl the parents had never met summed up a typical grievance. 'I'm fed up with everybody living off the fathead of the land—me,' he said. 'Had I pulled the trick my son did, my father would've told me that if I wanted to be a big man and sleep with a woman every night I'd have to go to work and support her. But I'm supposed to be glad that my son is a manly chap who likes girls. Hell, so do I, but nobody ever paid the freight for me like a kept man.'

"This may seem far-fetched or even offensive to many people, but the father's resentment stemmed in part from envy of his son's sexual vigor. There is a similar conflict called cosmetic rivalry between a mother and daughter. When a suitor calls on the girl, the mother primps and coquets as though the date is with her. She insists she turns on the charm simply to make a favorable impression for the daughter's sake, but she unconsciously is trying to demonstrate that she still is attractive to young men. There is such an absurd emphasis on the youth cult in this country that middle-aged parents wind up begrudging sexually mature children the pleasures of the marriage bed."

As the complexities of human motivation are unraveled, it is increasingly evident that criticism of Americans' compulsion for keeping up with the Joneses has been misinterpreted as a competition for social status. It is, rather, a desire to conform to the mores and attitudes of their groups and, like all cultural forces, this compliance is dictated by expediency. It is very well to exhort a man to assert his individuality by giving free rein to his convictions and aspirations, but a dissenter who flouts conventional conduct runs the risk of estranging himself from his neighbors and, in fact, fragmentizing the unity of the community. There is psychological security as well as physical safety in numbers.

Europeans who do not understand America's unique social structure always have ridiculed our obsession with "normal" behavior, particularly in the areas of sex. One notable exception was Alexis de Tocqueville, whose remarkably perceptive study, *Democracy in America,* was published in 1835. De Tocqueville saw that conformity of manners and attitudes was essential for survival in a sprawling country that was a loose confederation of settlements isolated by vast stretches of wilderness.

The pioneers who pushed beyond the frontiers of civilization had to possess a high degree of self-sufficiency, yet they were dependent on neighbors for protection against hostile intruders, for cooperation in clearing their land, building their homes and harvesting their crops and for assistance in delivering their babies and nursing their sick. Above all, they needed companionship to combat loneliness. Anthony Trollope said man can endure pain and fear better than boredom—an observation that since has been corroborated by such diverse investigators as space scientists, specialists in brainwashing and bartenders.

The United States today has the largest population in the Western world, but it still retains many characteristics of a pioneer society. The frontiers now are the proliferating suburbs of metropolitan areas where more than half the white, middle-class population lives—briefly. The average American couple moves fourteen times during their marriage. Our open society is more mobile than ever, due to the decentralization of old industries and the development of new ones, the massive migration of Negroes to the North and whites to the West, the shortage of moderate-priced urban housing, the dislocations caused by military service and the deterioration of public services—especially schools—in large cities.

Constant moving into strange surroundings inevitably produces a feeling of rootlessness, the loss of a sense of belonging, that is so necessary for emotional security. Each new location takes the family farther away from relatives and old friends who could be relied upon to lend a helping hand in emergencies. It is imperative, therefore, to cultivate acquaintances in the new community for sociability and assistance, and people gravitate to strangers with similar interests more readily than they accept outsiders with customs that are alien to them. The pressures on suburbanites to conform to their neighbors' mode of living are throwbacks psychologically to the influences that molded group attitudes and habits in frontier towns early in the nation's history.

Suburbs are like undeveloped outposts in another respect. Most of them have sprung up since World War II; virtually every adult is a first-generation settler. There are no entrenched social leaders whose positions stem from family prestige, inherited wealth or cultural attainments. The field is wide open to all comers, and the pacesetters are the *nouveaux riches,* who make the biggest splashes entertaining and introducing ostentatious fads. There is a natural tendency by new arrivals seeking acceptance in the community to imitate the In crowd, an expensive pastime that inveigles them into extravagances beyond their means. Once they are caught up in the social whirl, it is impossible to get off the merry-go-round and reduce expenses without losing face. It can be done in the privacy of big cities, where friends are seen infrequently and there is a wide choice of diversions, but people live under such close scrutiny in tightly integrated suburbs that retrenchments are noticed immediately.

Clashes over money between couples caught up in the competition of the suburbs are aggravated in middle age by a deeper conflict that gradually leads to a breakdown in marital relations. Although we are concerned chiefly with the male's sexual problems, it must be recognized that the strains of suburban life are rougher on his wife. Sex is the most reciprocal of all human relationships. What enhances or hinders one partner's enjoyment directly affects the other's gratification.

A woman who relished the excitement and mental stimulation of a city before she moved to suburbia never completely shakes off the feeling that she is trapped in a stultifying rut of domestic chores. She has no real roots in the community—no sense of personal involvement with acquaintances who happen to live in the vicinity. Neither has a man, but his work and contacts with other people are an escape from the confining routine of chauffering children, marketing, struggling with balky appliances and small talk that does not vary from one year to the next. A suburban wife with grown children who no longer need constant supervision is at loose ends—and at cross-purposes with her middle-aged husband. She looks to him for relief from the intellectual vacuum in which she has been stranded all day; he comes home exhausted by his job and commuting. She wants him to take her out or at least talk to her; he wants to unwind with a quiet drink and stay home. She resents his neglect of her and retaliates by rejecting him in bed, the storm warning of a foundering marriage.

"I wouldn't know whether there is more infidelity in suburbia than elsewhere, but I do know it is increasing sharply," says Dr. Victor Balaban, a veteran director of the Family Counseling Service's field offices in Westchester County bordering New York City. "When you speak of infidelity, you always assume husbands are the guilty parties, but they must have accomplices, and restless wives are taking the initiative in encouraging affairs. They are much more outspoken than they used to be in criticizing their husbands' sexual inadequacy. I continually hear the same complaint: 'He expects me to be nice to him in bed on Saturday night after he ignores me all week.'

"Sexual incompatability in couples who have been married a long time is, of course, a symptom of other emotional disturbances. In the suburbs it usually can be traced to the competitive pressures that warp people's sense of values. It has reached the point where frustrated parents are competing vicariously through their children. They go into debt for elaborate weddings, confirmations and coming-out parties, to buy their kids cars and send them to private schools to better their chances of acceptance by an Ivy League college. Getting into a college with a solid academic tradition is not enough. The parents are crushed if it is not an Ivy League college with a glamorous reputation.

"A very common problem is the under-achiever, a bright, talented student who gets poor grades in high school. Five out of six are boys. Fathers who look upon sons as extensions of themselves put so much pressure on the boys to be Number One that the kids stop trying to reach more reasonable goals. Socially ambitious mothers push daughters into loveless marriages with rich boys before other girls hook them first. Then the mothers are shocked when the marriages end in divorce.

"Parents defend their excesses by arguing that they are only trying to give their children every possible advantage. What they do not realize is that they are doing too much, overcompensating for their feeling of guilt for failing as mature adults."

Self-doubt feeds on unfounded fears—particularly on a false sense of sexual guilt.

# 7

# The Great Taboo

***

"IT IS SURELY NO SECRET THAT, DESPITE ALL THAT HAS BEEN said and done scientifically, the popular attitude toward sex still is largely a mixture of salaciousness and shame," Dr. Karl Menninger observed a quarter of a century ago. Our fund of sexual knowledge has increased enormously since then, but we continue to compound guilt-ridden neuroses by deferring to a repressive moral code that does not acknowledge the positive values of sex.

We know subjectively that love and love-making are synonymous in a good marriage—that a strong sexual attraction between a husband and wife is the catalyst that elevates marriage from an arid social partnership to a spiritual communion. Yet all we hear is that preoccupation with sex is responsible for the "soaring" divorce rate—which actually has dropped in recent years to the pre-World War II level. Perhaps the most persistent fallacy in general circulation is the assertion that one marriage in every four ends in divorce in the United States. This figure is a gross distortion, because it relates the number of divorces to the new marriages in a given year when, in fact, current divorces dissolve unions that have lasted as long as thirty or forty years. The true statistical ratio is one divorce for every 110 married couples.

Hand-wringers who deplore the immorality allegedly rampant today fail to recognize that the marriages which do survive are richer in affection and companionship and aspirations for children than ever before. There are no statistics to prove this, but Havelock Ellis could have been right when he said, "Emotional reactions are the only facts." It must be love that impels the typical middle-aged man to keep on contending with mounting pressures in order to give his family the material advantages he feels they deserve.

Instead of profiting from new insights into the libido, we listen to blatant drivel that puts us on the defensive about our "mania" for sex. A flagrant example of cheap sensationalism was a widely reprinted article from an April, 1965, issue of *The New Statesman,* ordinarily a sober British magazine, written by Malcolm Muggeridge, a former editor of *Punch.* Muggeridge, who is making a career of exposing concupiscence even if he has to invent it, wrote in part:

"America is drenched, if not submerged, in sex. It permeates every corner and cranny of life, from birth to the grave. . . . Dating begins at nine years old. Tiny tots wear padded bras, paint their faces and howl like randy hyenas at the Beatles. Young lovers arm themselves with birth pills and the *Kama Sutra.* . . . Middle-age couples swap partners and disturb the peace of suburban nights with their strident love cries. The old, their dentures gleaming, look lecherously around or doze in their bath chairs over *Candy* or *The Tropic of Cancer.* Even the dead are curled and scented for a tumble in the grave."

Muggeridge's sexual fantasies seem to be activated by money, a powerful aphrodisiac to self-appointed watchdogs of public morals. He was in the vanguard of British pundits who rushed into print deploring the Empire's ignoblest hour when John Profumo, England's Secretary of State for War, resigned in 1963 after admitting to indiscretions in the busy bed of Christine Keeler, a London harlot. Muggeridge branded London "the filthiest town in the world." Novelist J. P. Priestley denounced the striptease clubs of Soho as egregious examples of the commercial eroticism that "now constitutes one of the worst features of Western civilization." Historian Arnold

Toynbee declared that obsession with sex would be the ruination of Judeo-Christian culture and drew gloomy parallels between the prevailing moral climate and the decadence that undermined ancient Greece and Rome.

At the height of the caterwauling, the voice of reason was sounded by Aldous Huxley, an Englishman with imposing intellectual credentials. In the last interview before his death in 1963, Huxley reminded his countrymen that devastating plagues of malaria rather than debauchery had sapped the vigor of the Greeks and Romans.

"I don't think I've ever met anybody who wasn't obsessed with sex in any country," he added. "Every highly urban civilization has to be obsessed with sex for the simple reason that it is out of touch with nature. The people are living in a particularly artificial world, a world of organization, and not the kind of world that one lives in the country. And the nearest approach to country life is, in fact, sex."

The furors over such scandals as the Profumo affair reflect the conflict between permissiveness and puritanism, the dominant moral force of the Christian ethic, that lies at the root of many sexual problems today. It is a wry commentary on society's ambivalence toward sex that we are assailed periodically by a sense of guilt for having cast off the hypocrisy of the past. The behavioral sciences of the twentieth century assure us that enjoyment of sex is a rewarding expression of a natural drive but, intimidated by religious injunctions against carnal excesses, we do not trust ourselves to draw the line between freedom and license.

If there is one thing we have learned it is that the sexual needs of individuals differ so tremendously that one man's frequency of intercourse may be tantamount to severe abstinence for a second man and complete abandonment to concupiscence for a third. Yet the criteria of "normal" desire are set arbitrarily by members of society who are the least active sexually—by elderly legislators, judges and clergymen. If everyone who ate more than an effete vegetarian was considered a glutton regardless of age, height, metabolism, bone structure and daily physical exertion, the blanket indictment would be as senseless as our code of sexual morality.

Laws governing sex are such a conglomeration of ignorance and medieval taboos that in half the states of America anyone who instructs children in the functions of the reproductive organs can be prosecuted for contributing to the delinquency of minors. In Oregon, to cite another absurd example, a man who takes an affectionate peck at his wife's cheek and happens to kiss her on the neck is guilty of "a crime against nature," a police-blotter euphemism for a perversion. In many rural areas an unmarried couple petting in a car can be held as common fornicators, and if the girl is under the age of consent the charge is statutory rape.

Although arrests on such technicalities are rare, the fact that the laws still are on the books attests to the leering attitudes we have inherited. The sexual urge is at once the most private and universal of all feelings, but man is not only a biological creature. He also is a social individual functioning within his cultural environment, the major determinant in his sexual mores.

Nothing would seem subject to less variation than the basic sexual technique, the position in coitus. Among English-speaking people and most Europeans, the male usually mounts the supine female—to the vast amusement of natives in the Southwest Pacific who derisively call it "the missionary position." Some years ago Clyde Kluckhohn, a Harvard anthropologist, made a study of the favored coital positions in 193 cultures and found that the commonest method of copulation was insertion from the rear, with the male squatting behind the prone female. In Western society this posture is regarded as a perversion when practiced regularly, but it can be defended biologically as the position used by all other mammals throughout nature.

It may disconcert the circumspect to learn that advanced civilizations of the ancient world considered the supine female a depraved reversal of her customary position—on top of the male. Thousands of friezes and drawings depicting coitus dating back to 3000 B.C. have been excavated in Mesopotamia, Egypt, India, China and Peru, and the overwhelming majority show the female in the superior position. It was so conventional among the Greeks and Romans that references to other procedures in heterosexual intercourse were found mainly in pornography.

Cultural conditioning also accounts for the differences in the female physical characteristics that arouse men. The chemistry of sexual attraction that makes one woman more desirable than another is a mysterious amalgam, but we know her face and figure are not always the principal elements. There are a lot of homely, dumpy girls, and most of them do get married.

High-caste Hindus, who go through an elaborate ritual of communicating love signals by manipulating the fingers, take a special interest in a woman's hands. A long, slender neck has an erotic effect on the Japanese, and although the Chinese have been prohibited from binding the feet of infant girls for more than half a century, a small, delicate foot still is highly prized. In Moslem countries, where respectable women did not appear unveiled in public until a generation ago, a man is excited by large, expressive eyes, once the only feature that was visible to him. Feminine allure is measured by obesity among certain African tribes. Girls are segregated at puberty and stuffed with sweet, fattening foods to enhance their value on the marriage market.

Throughout the West a pair of trim legs will catch the eye of every man, but it shifts to different erogenous areas as national boundaries are crossed. In the United States, England and the Commonwealth countries, attention is focused on the breasts. The French and Italian, while properly appreciative of *la belle poitrine,* are more intrigued by a well-rounded *derrière.* Germans and Slavs prefer women with broad hips and heavy thighs. Spaniards and Latin Americans have catholic tastes; they go for any provocative curve between the neck and the knees.

The multimillion-dollar deodorant industry in the United States is a more modest operation in middle Europe, where the odor of perspiration is believed to be a powerful aphrodisiac. At rural dances it is customary for a man to hold a handkerchief under his armpit until his partner coquettishly asks for it to wipe her brow. In a corresponding ploy, many upper-class European women did not shave their armpits until a few years ago. The growth under the arms was considered a sex lure suggestive of pubic hair. When the Folies-Bergère was first invited to perform in London, the French impresario threatened to cancel the engagement rather than comply with the English producer's order that the girls shave under their arms.

Geographical differences in reactions to sexual stimuli are superficial, of course. An Asian will turn and stare at a shapely girl wearing a short skirt and a tight sweater as quickly as an Occidental, which explains why Western fashions are supplanting the kimono, sari and jubbah throughout the Orient. But the basic attitudes inculcated by religion, the most important cultural influence on the individual's sexuality, are as difficult to change as the course of a glacier.

The religions that originated in the East recognized and clearly defined the role of sex in a happy, constructive life. The ancient Hebrews sanctioned polygamy in the belief that a vigorous man's physical desires could not be completely satisfied by one woman. A high premium was placed on the virginity of a marriageable girl, but the Hebrews were tolerant of premarital affairs between engaged couples. Buddhism stressed the pleasures of physical love in a blissful marriage and specifically charged the wife with responsibility for contributing to its erotic excitement. A cornerstone of Confucius' philosophy of the "good life" was a harmonious conjugal relationship as a unifying force within the family. The Greeks and Romans attributed human passions to their gods and gradually turned festivals honoring them into debauches. Although Mohammedans are bound by the strictest prohibitions any religion imposes on other appetites, Turkish and Arab culture is permeated with a sexual mystique that always has seemed obsessive to the Western world.

Only Christianity fears the libido as though it is a dangerous beast that will run amok unless it is kept in a cage of rigid repressions. The early Christians did not consider sex intrinsically sinful until the fifth century when St. Augustine, a libertine before his conversion, began preaching that even within marriage, copulation was an evil, although a necessary one for the procreation of children. For a thousand years the Catholic Church, strongly influenced by St. Augustine's views, fulminated against the temptations of the flesh. As Lewis Mumford has caustically observed, "Even Thomas More, a sensitive, enlightened man, spoke of sexual intercourse as if it were on the same level with urination: mere relief of a distended organ."

The rise of humanism during the Renaissance, exalting the social and esthetic facets of man's nature, revived the ideal of romantic love and gave sex a new interpretation that clashed head-on with Catholic dogma. "A woman not possessed of a light and rare grace can no more abstain from a man than from eating, drinking or sleeping or other natural functions. Likewise a man cannot abstain from a woman." The advocate of that hedonism was not Dante, Petrarch, Chaucer or any other lyric poet who rejected the Church's dictum that worldly pleasures were sinful. He was Martin Luther, who married Katharina von Bora, a former nun, four years after he was excommunicated in 1521. Even the austere Puritans of New England, who looked upon lust as Satan's special trap for the unwary, recognized that sex was a natural component of love.

Culprits found guilty of fornication were fined £10 in Plymouth, but if they were engaged the penalty was only £5.

It is at once curious and revealing that the lower clergy and orthodox laymen of all Western sects today are interpreting the religious doctrines governing sexual behavior far more rigorously than the hierarchy. An increasing number of Protestant theologians are inclined to agree with Granville Fisher, a psychologist who says, "Sex is not a moral question. For answers you don't turn to a body of absolutes. The criterion should not be, 'Is it morally right or wrong?' but 'Is it socially feasible, is it personally healthy and rewarding, will it enrich human life?' "

One of the most startling ideological shifts of the twentieth century has been the acknowledgement by the Catholic Church that sexual desire is a concomitant of conjugal love. In 1951, Pope Pius XII declared it was proper that "husband and wife shall find pleasure and happiness of mind and body." The Ecumenical Council, which convened in Rome from 1962 through 1965 to modernize Church policy, reaffirmed Pope Pius's encyclical by ruling that sexuality is not purely a biological function but an important spiritual dimension of man. Such controversial questions as the Council's endorsement of religious freedom and a statement deploring anti-Semitism made bigger headlines, but another thorny issue touched off heated debates behind the scenes in the closing weeks of the assembly. It was a petition by eighty-one prominent laymen from twelve countries to abolish the vow of celibacy for priests.

Although Pope Paul VI banned public discussion of the proposal, George Weller, of the *Chicago Daily News,* reported: "The marriage of priests has joined contraception as an issue too troubled to allow open declarations by bishops at the Vatican Council, but consequently it is debated the more fiercely in the uncontrollable free forums around St. Peter's Basilica." The petition was supported by Peter Paul

Koop, a Dutch bishop from Brazil, who asserted that there is an "alarming" shortage of priests in some parts of the world, because many men are unable to remain celibate. He pointed out that the Greek Orthodox Church, which accepts married men for ordainment, has no problem recruiting candidates. Bishop Koop concluded by warning the Council: "To save the Church in Latin America it is necessary to introduce a married clergy as soon as possible." A poll privately circulated in Rome indicated that the majority of one thousand Brazilian priests were unhappy about their unmarried status. Another survey suggested that many Latin-American priests who found abstinence no problem were either emotionally immature or latent homosexuals.

Further opposition to the Church's law of clerical celibacy was disclosed by *Jubilee,* a Catholic magazine in the United States. In October, 1966, it reported that in a poll of priests who were subscribers, two-thirds favored a reappraisal of the ancient discipline. The priests ranged in age from twenty-seven to seventy-six. "Personally, I think celibacy makes me a more Christlike priest, but more and more I can appreciate that married life and priesthood are not incompatible," a fifty-seven-year-old pastor wrote. A priest twenty years younger said that celibacy was both widely admired and widely misunderstood by the Catholic laity. It is, he said, a source of loneliness and tension and is responsible for the "crankiness of many older priests."

So, after seventy-five years, dissenting elements in the Catholic Church finally are admitting tacitly that Sigmund Freud was right when he said it was impossible for a virile man to sublimate his libido. When he advanced this thesis, critics argued that it was disproved by priests who voluntarily took vows of celibacy. Freud retorted that the sex drives of such men were so low their sacrifices in renouncing sex were negligible—a curt dismissal that brought him the bitter enmity of the contemporary Catholic clergy.

Education has cushioned the shock of another bombshell exploded by Freud: his contention that it was absurd to condemn a practice as universal, and as harmless, as masturbation. While he was developing his psychoanalytic technique, Freud found many patients were suffering from an oppressive sense of guilt for having masturbated in adolescence and for reverting to it occasionally as adults in preference to heterosexual intercourse. Their anxiety could be traced to a treatise on masturbation written in 1758 by S. A. Tissot, a Frenchman who attributed to autoeroticism every malady from cancer to carbuncles and, for good measure, warned that it could lead to insanity. In the 1890's physicians still were citing Tissot's mishmash of myths as an authoritative scientific study.

Dr. A. A. Brill told an amusing story to illustrate the "masturbation complex" that plagued even well-informed young men at the turn of the century. In his senior year at the Columbia University medical school a clinic on the subject was conducted by a Professor Taylor, a specialist in genitourinary diseases. He started by declaring, "Gentlemen, I think that all these ideas about masturbation are exaggerated. I do not believe masturbation produces insanity. I do not think it does any harm at all."

"At this," Brill recalled, "the whole class burst into spontaneous applause, so strong was the feeling of relief with which we heard these remarks."

After the lecture, an elderly physician accosted Taylor. "You said that everybody masturbates. I would like to take exception to that. I never did."

"Well," Taylor retorted, "you missed a good thing."

Everyone assumed that masturbation was confined almost entirely to males until the publication in 1929 of a survey by Dr. Katharine B. Davis of the sex lives of 2200 women college graduates. She reported that 65 percent of the subjects admitted they had masturbated at one time or another —and Kinsey later extended the time far beyond the previously suspected limit. His interviews revealed that the incidence of masturbation among women—married, single, divorced or widowed—increases after the age of twenty-five and remains fairly constant until sixty. Although Kinsey's statistics indicated that women who practice self-stimulation resort to it on an average of only once or twice a month, it is significant that their overall increase contrasts sharply with the corresponding figures for males, which gradually drop after adolescense and continue to decline steadily with age until there is a resumption when no other outlet is available.

There are several reasons why mature women masturbate more frequently than girls—a direct reversal of the male pattern. A woman loses her inhibitions with sexual experience and becomes more responsive to erotic stimulation. As she approaches middle age, the imbalance between the male and female sex drives may impel her to find an outlet beyond coitus. Nature, so artful in complementing most of the other differences between the sexes, slipped up badly with the libido. The male reaches the peak of his potency at twenty, but the female's desire is strongest at forty and continues on a high level for another fifteen years. As a consequence, she may turn to self-gratification when her partner is unable to bring her to an orgasm.

Although masturbation hardly is a suitable topic of conversation at dinner parties, only the ignorant continue to regard it as a vile habit paving the way to perdition. Modern marriage manuals approve of mutual masturbation for young, inexperienced couples on their honeymoon, because it is their most familiar sexual outlet, and further recommend that a wife bring her husband to a climax manually during menstruation and late pregnancy. Some physicians and marriage counselors suggest that masturbation can be helpful in equalizing the disparate sexual demands of couples and argue that it is a preferred substitute to flirting with adultery when a husband and wife are separated for long periods.

Intellectually, we recognize that every normal adult living in a normal environment needs periodic releases of sexual impulses through coitus, masturbation or involuntary nocturnal emissions, a natural safety valve, until old age or infirmity stifles the spark of desire. Psychologically, though, we have been unable to throw off in one short generation the "mixture of salaciousness and shame" that has characterized the Christian attitude toward sex for fifteen hundred years.

The conflict between practice and preachment, between what we do privately and what we are told publicly we should do, has been intensified by drastic changes in the cultural climate. Recent decisions by the United States Supreme Court permit virtually everything to be published or exhibited on the stage and the screen except the crudest, hard-core pornography. Scatology no longer is proscribed simply because it is obscene. Any peddler of smut can get off the hook of censorship with phony moralizing. The trick is to dwell on the clinical details of a character's depravity for three hundred pages or two hours, then have the wretch realize in the final scene that sex without love is carnal, whereupon all is forgiven by his long-suffering spouse and the authorities.

Nudity in the movies, formerly confined to fleeting rear views, gradually has made a 180-degree turn in foreign and Hollywood productions. Dramatic pictures—not documentaries—released in neighborhood theaters are showing front shots of women uncovered above the waist and it is, presumably, just a matter of time before the camera, and legal bars, are dropped lower. Films made in Sweden by Ingmar Bergman with explicit close-ups of women during coitus, masturbation, incest and Lesbian by-play have been seen in the United States under the seals of state approval. On Broadway, the opening scenes in a number of plays have shown a couple in bed to indicate immediately, as drama critic Walter Kerr whimsically explains, that the male lead is not a homosexual.

Girlie magazines openly displayed on newsstands contain

photographs that would have sent a surreptitious distributor to jail a few years ago. The erotic passages and four-letter words in *Ulysses, Lady Chatterley's Lover,* Henry Miller's effusions and World War II novels, which once sent censors rushing to the courts for injunctions, appear mild compared to current descriptions of sexual aberrations that Krafft-Ebing referred to only in Latin.

Pornography always has been more offensive to good taste than to morals, because it is as dull as the switches on a stale joke even when treated by master stylists. During the eighteenth century some of the most eminent writers in France —Voltaire, Montesquieu, Diderot, Rousseau, de la Bretonne, La Mettrie—wrote pornography for money or murkier designs. One of the few works with any literary merit—perhaps the only one—was *Les Liaisons Dangereuses* by Choderlos de Laclos, who later was committed to the madhouse at Charenton while the Marquis de Sade was an inmate there. *Les Liaisons Dangereuses,* which was adapted into a French film in a contemporary setting several years ago, traced the degeneracy of two aristocratic libertines who maliciously ruined other people, and eventually themselves, through sadism, perversions and sexual excesses. It actually was a moral book that underscored the difference between good and evil, but it was read mainly for its purple passages of the corruption in the court of Louis XVI.

Distorted attitudes toward sex now are camouflaged by a new, avant-garde facade. The influx of homosexuals into the performing arts is infesting the theater with themes that are contemptuous of women, marriage and conventional relationships. The deviate's fear of women has produced a steady run of plays that depict them as destructive neurotics and/or bitches. The technical facility of a few leading playwrights who attack sexual conformity has been applauded by a pretentious coterie that elevates style over substance, but their sick social outlook finally was denounced by Stanley Kauffmann, then the drama critic of *The New York Times,* in 1966. After stating it was common knowledge in show business that "three of the most successful American playwrights of the last twenty years are (reputed) homosexuals," Kauffmann declared:

"We have all had very much more than enough of the materials so often presented by the three writers in question: the viciousness toward women, the lurid violence that seems a sublimation of social hatred, the transvestite sexual exhibitionism that has the same sneering exploitation of its audience that every club stripper has behind her smile."

The influence of homosexuals extends far beyond the stage. All their hits—and their batting averages are impressive—have been made into movies, prompting cruder imitations in the same genre. In recent years there have been mounting complaints that a "homosexual Mafia" has infiltrated television and set up enclaves within the networks that adulterate the tone and content of dramatic shows by caricaturing married people. In the stupefying situation comedies that comprise the bulk of TV programing, Pop is an amiable idiot who submits meekly to Mom, a virago who apparently is highy indignant that she is unable to produce children spontaneously through parthenogenesis.

There is a Gresham's Law in sex as well as economics. Emphasis on the prurient aspects of sex eventually depreciates the emotional fulfillment a man and a woman find in a good physical relationship. "Our culture is going through a sexual crisis," says Dr. Mary S. Calderone, executive director of the Sex Information and Education Council. "There is a tremendous amount of confusion about the uses and purposes of sex—all the way from those who think that sex is simply for fun to those who think it is so holy no one should ever have it."

The conflict is not confined to inexperienced youngsters caught in a tug of war between morality and the libido. Middle-aged people frequently are strongly affected by the whither-are-we-drifting alarums raised by critics who seize upon every public scandal as proof that unbridled sex is plunging us deeper into decadence. The charge is preposterous, but constant repetition of it may be so disturbing to people going through an emotional crisis of middle age that they condemn all sexual activity and renounce it for themselves.

When a couple with a family is divorced or separated after some twenty years, the common assumption is that they were incompatible for a long time but delayed the break for the sake of the children. The reverse is true in a surprising number of cases. The trouble develops when a child approaching adulthood begins to step out socially and arouses the parents' guilt feelings of their own behavior at that age. A father, remembering his own early explorations, worries that an irrepressible impulse will result in a pregnancy forcing his son or daughter into a disastrous marriage. Subconsciously, he curtails intercourse with his wife to expiate his own youthful indiscretions. For the same reason the wife may become frigid. If there are no overt complications the parents may become reconciled to their child's affair as part of the maturing process. With all the talk about homosexuality in circulation, the father may even be relieved that his son likes girls. A mother's concern is more intense, however, if a daughter is involved.

The present generation of middle-aged women was the first to grow up in the permissive atmosphere brought by the sexual revolution of the 1920's. They were the first to go out on unchaperoned dates, the first to admit that they necked with boys, and the first to deny virginity as a prerequisite for marriage. They shrilly rejected the double standard, but few girls were promiscuous tramps. The overwhelming majority of those who had affairs married the first or second man with whom they went to bed. They could not cast off completely fifteen centuries of Christian morality.

"What is bred in the bone will never come out of the flesh."

A woman who rebelled against sexual restraints as a girl is a prisoner of her conscience when she suspects a daughter is having a premarital affair. A son's misbehavior can be rationalized as typical of the predatory male, but a mother sees a reflection of her own sins in a daughter's lapses. Her feeling of guilt may be so acute that she repudiates sex and stops intercourse with her husband. Shame prevents her from confiding in him and he, interpreting her frigidity as rejection of him, looks for affection elsewhere, and another marriage drifts toward the rocks.

A complication seldom encountered years ago is the curious reaction of some parents to a child's marriage. Their rate of intercourse drops after the wedding and remains low until it picks up again with the arrival of a grandchild. They have read so many stories about sexual maladjustments among young people that anxiety over the stability of a child's marriage curbs their own desire for coitus. The birth of a baby proves only that a man and a woman slept together once, of course, but it seems to give the grandparents assurance that the newlyweds' sexual relationship is mutually satisfactory. If there is no child within two or three years, the older couple's self-recriminations have been known to lead to a permanent suspension of intercourse.

Whenever the issue of sex and morality is debated, attention is focused almost exclusively on adolescents and college students teetering on a tightrope between old codes and changing mores. It can be argued that experienced adults have more difficulty maintaining their equilibrium. Confused youngsters can rightfully disclaim culpability for the conditions they have inherited, but middle-aged people cannot fall back on that defense. They are trustees of public morality and, skeptics to the contrary, many regard it as a solemn obligation. Only psychopaths are totally devoid of a sense of responsibility for their actions. If people are told constantly that they are contributing to the moral delinquency of society, they eventually turn against sex as an instrument of corruption.

Comes a pertinent question: Has our alleged obsession with sex resulted in a serious erosion of morals? Are we more depraved because *Fanny Hill* can be bought for seventy-five cents off an open paperback rack instead of costing $10 for a pirated edition sold under the counter? If we really are going to hell in a handbasket pursuing pleasure, how do critics explain our increasing involvement with social reforms?

Is nudity in the movies and strip joints more offensive to decency than the red-light districts that formerly flourished in every town under police protection? Organized vice has practically disappeared in the United States, and the gag that amateurs have driven the professionals out of business was an old chestnut when Messalina, the slut of Rome, was a girl. The Mafia, once the overlord of prostitution, has been concentrating on more lucrative rackets in gambling, narcotics and commercial extortion for thirty years. The fifty-dollar call girl is not so much the product of inflation as obsolescence, like the fancy price a car buff will pay for a rococo accessory from a Stutz Bearcat.

Streetwalkers have been banned in England, France and Italy within the last decade. Although enforcement of the laws is something less than airtight, the traffic in illicit sex in Europe is the lowest since the Industrial Revolution gave the working man money to buy it. Hamburg's and Amsterdam's notorious waterfronts are the last pockets of freewheeling brothels on the Continent. In 1850, the police admitted there were ten thousand prostitutes in London, or one for every one hundred men. In 1959, a commission appointed by Parliament estimated there were eight thousand prostitutes in London soliciting a male population that had tripled during the preceding century.

The sexual excesses condemned today are mischievous escapades compared to the debauchery of the Victorian Era, that fraudulent symbol of rectitude. Peers in the House of Lords who piously deplored the drunkenness and fornication of the lower class were masters of the revels in the bawdyhouses. When a retired military officer was said to have died with his boots on, it was tactful not to ask questions. The doughty old gentleman might have expired from amatory exploits in a brothel.

Sons of aristocratic families constantly were sued by prostitutes who claimed they had been fleeced of their earnings to pay gambling debts. Oscar Wilde, the arbiter of elegance in London society, was imprisoned for sodomy. Sir Charles Dilke, who was being groomed to succeed Gladstone as Prime Minister, was forced to resign after a lurid divorce trial in 1886. Mrs. Donald Crawford, the wife of an M.P., charged that Sir Charles had seduced her shortly after her honeymoon and thereafter she had visited him in his home four mornings a week. Mrs. Crawford further testified that Sir Charles had induced her to engage in "unmentionable" sexual practices with a young servant girl in his household.

The most outrageous scandal was the Crown's intervention behind the scenes of a divorce suit involving the Prince of Wales, later Edward VII. In 1870, Sir Charles Mordaunt, M.P., accused his twenty-one-year-old wife Harriet of adultery with Viscount Cole, Sir Frederick Johnstone and "others." Every scullery maid in England knew that the unnamed correspondent was Edward.

Harriet admitted in open court that she had been intimate with Edward, the father of four children. A maid and a butler testified that Edward often visited Her Ladyship at home while Sir Charles was in Parliament. Sir Charles said he had warned his wife to stay away from Wales, because he had heard "in various quarters certain circumstances connected with the Prince's character which caused me to make that remark."

After such an unprecedented public aspersion of a member of the royal family, Edward could not avoid answering a subpoena as a witness in the trial, marking the first time an heir to the throne ever had appeared on the stand. He denied under questioning by his counsel "any improper familiarity or criminal act with Lady Mordaunt." A battery of doctors testified that Harriet had lost her mind and was suffering from "puerperal mania" following the birth of a child threatened with blindness. Her confession that Lord Cole was the father of the child was blandly brushed off as an hallucination. The court dismissed the suit on grounds of Harriet's insanity. Five years later Sir Charles quietly was granted a divorce.

The English public, like Queen Victoria, was not amused by the trial—although for a different reason. Edward was sent abroad on a vague diplomatic mission after he was hissed at the theater and the races. His subjects were tolerant of his philandering, but they could not condone his lying under oath. It simply wasn't done by a gentleman.

John Profumo had a loftier sense of noblesse oblige than the blue-blooded Victorians. Although he denied at first his association with a call girl—as any gentleman would—he was not guilty of perjury like Edward nor did he embarrass the government in a sordid trial like Dilke. The wild rumors that Profumo had jeopardized national security by exposing himself to blackmail in a bed familiar to a Russian intelligence agent were strictly Fleet Street inventions. Profumo's gravest offense against the public interest was his undiscriminating choice of female companions, but he was pilloried for violating the taboo that equates sex with sin.

Our society is so fearful of sex that it is easier for a schoolboy to procure a heroin "fix" or a goofball than a prostitute. We prosecute vice more grimly than violence, but we impose the harshest punishment on ourselves.

# 8

# Impotence

※ ※ ※

ONE OF THE MOST CONTROVERSIAL, AND ENVIED, PIONEERS IN psychiatry was Dr. Wilhelm Stekel, a Viennese who was a disciple of Freud but later broke with him. The envy was prompted largely by Stekel's income from psychoanalyzing more than ten thousand patients—an incredible caseload that never has been approached. In addition to his enormous private practice, Stekel published nine lengthy studies on sexual disorders between 1920 and 1932. The books still are valuable reference works, but conservative contemporaries condemned them as potboilers to exploit the public's interest in sex.

Stekel was accused of exaggerating the prevalence of sexual neuroses to promote the sale of his books, a charge that continually embroiled him with critics after the publication of *Impotence in the Male*. "The percentage of relatively impotent men cannot be placed too high," he wrote. "In my experience, hardly half of all civilized men enjoy normal potency." Stekel's estimate no longer is considered excessive by the profession. More importantly, his interpretation of impotence is the universally accepted guide for early recognition and treatment of symptoms that foreshadow sexual problems, especially in middle-aged men.

When a man is asked what is meant by impotence, he invariably answers that it is the inability to achieve an erection, but this definition has been discarded as an incomplete diagnosis of the condition. Lack of desire for intercourse is an indication of impotence. So is premature ejaculation and failure to maintain a strong erection until a woman has been brought to a satisfactory orgasm. In fact, going through the motions of coitus mechanically, without deriving intense pleasure from it, is a form of impotence and a preliminary to more pronounced manifestations if the apathy persists.

By these criteria, the man who boasts that he never has had a disappointment in bed is an incurable romantic or a victim of self-delusion. Sexual performance is affected by so many physical and intangible factors that it is impossible to reach a high peak of excitement in every experience. Occasional slip-ups can be discounted as accidents induced by fatigue or nervous tension, but the trouble is that temporary failure often is magnified by anxiety or ignorance and tends to become self-perpetuating. One frustrating episode can start a chain reaction that undermines a man's confidence so severely that inhibitions eventually stifle his libido.

Stekel, who also did an exhaustive study of frigidity in women, concluded that impotence is a far more common disability with a harsher emotional impact. "Impotence is a target for much jest; in the theatre, in proverbs and in obscenities it is treated as an important erotic theme," he wrote. "The frigid woman, however, receives only slight attention in literature; public opinion even elevates her infirmity to the rank of a virtue and gives it a heroic varnish, whereas the virtuous, impotent man succumbs to the curse of ridicule."

Impotence is such a devastating blow to a man's ego that it has been known to drive some victims to suicide, but the salient point is that it can be cured in the overwhelming majority of cases—and not necessarily by psychiatric treatment. Fully 98 percent are psychogenic, or originate in the mind. The purely physical causes, apart from injury to the genitals or venereal infection, are limited to a few chronic diseases—leukemia, tuberculosis, anemia and sometimes diabetes. To repeat Dr. William Ferber's maxim, "What happens above a man's neck is vastly more important than what happens below his belt."

Instant self-therapy can be effected, for example, by reading a piece in a newspaper on the jet lag, the curious feeling of disorientation that hits plane passengers who cross different time zones within a few hours. Specialists who have studied the phenomenon attribute it to the disruption of an inner sense of timing that governs the heart rate, temperature and metabolism, making travelers vaguely lethargic and distracted for a day or two before they adjust to a new schedule. Government officials and business executives attending important conferences in foreign countries now make a practice of arriving on the scene thirty-six hours in advance to counteract the jet lag, technically called asynchronosis.

This simple explanation can dispel the anxiety of a man who does a good deal of traveling on business and is worried by his sluggish response in making love to his wife on the first night he returns from a long trip. His weak or premature orgasms might arouse some suspicion that he is losing his potency if he did not know that the jet lag upsets his nervous and digestive systems. Common sense tells him his sexual mechanism is affected in a similar manner and that it is advisable to wait a night or two before resuming marital relations, a solution that promptly relieves his doubts.

The overriding stumbling block in treating middle-aged men who fear they are slipping into impotence is that each one is convinced his problem is unique. A man who has been addicted to the numbers game throughout his adult life associates an active libido so intimately with virility that he is ashamed to admit that his rate of intercourse is decreasing. A physician could quickly assure him that he is going through an entirely normal tapering-off process, but by the time he seeks professional advice his withdrawal from sex usually is so far advanced that restoring his self-confidence is a major reclamation project.

A few years ago the favorite author among show-business people who congregated in a bar in New York was, quite improbably, Sigmund Freud. Their esoteric taste in literature developed after a press agent in his late forties, noted for his success with accommodating ladies, had a prostate operation. The prostate is a gland with a minor function in the male's genital apparatus, but to most men any impairment of it has a grim connotation of sexual disability.

The clique began speaking of poor old Charlie as though he was an invalid condemned permanently to celibacy. While he was convalescing, visitors studiously refrained from referring to women in deference to their stricken's comrade's sad plight. A friend was upbraided for sending Charlie a risqué get-well card. The boys cut down on drinking, made rueful, self-deprecatory jokes about their waning physical powers and sounded like a convention of hypochondriacs comparing their symptoms.

The wake for Charlie's departed love life—and, inferentially, their own—had been going on for several weeks when one of the cronies returned from a trip to Hollywood with a paperback collection of Freud's lectures that he had picked up on the plane. In thumbing through it, he had come across a sentence that was peculiarly reassuring. The others devoured it as avidly as schoolboys poring over a titillating passage in *Lady Chatterley's Lover*. It read: "If a practicing psychoanalyst asks himself what disorder he is most often called upon to remedy, he is obliged to reply—apart from anxiety in all its many forms—psychical impotence."

Everyone immediately felt better. The complaints disappeared, and there was a fresh crop of amiable lies about exploits in the boudoir. Freud's statement was calculated to arouse apprehension by emphasizing the high incidence of impotence, yet the men who imagined they were threatened by it actually were relieved to learn so many others were under the same shadow.

Stekel spoke of the "will to impotence," an unconscious avoidance of sex to escape masculine responsibilities. The confirmed bachelor who sighs plaintively and says he would love to get married if he found the right girl fools no one except gullible maidens. He invents obstacles to marriage to cover up his fear that he will be unable to gratify a woman in a permanent relationship. He makes dutiful passes at unattached females to avert the suspicion that he is "queer," but he always breaks off an affair before he reaches the point of no return from a binding commitment.

The married middle-aged man who abruptly curtails marital relations for no ostensible reason presents a more complex problem. If he is not advancing economically while friends are prospering, he may feel that his failure is penalizing his wife socially and he does not deserve her favors in bed. His withdrawal from her is a wistful expression of love, but it is a sign of hostility when the circumstances are reversed.

The conflict arising from a husband who depends on his wife's money or family connections for his status no longer is peculiar to upper-class marriages. It has spread to the middle-class of the Affluent Society, especially among men now in their late forties who married immediately after military service in World War II. Spurred by the urgency to make up lost time and opportunities, they sought shortcuts to the security that was doubly attractive after the uncertainty of war. For many who had been too young to settle on careers before going into the armed forces, the most convenient footholds were in businesses owned by fathers-in-law.

"What appeared to be a promising setup for a young fellow often proved a bad mistake," Dr. George Goldman, a New York psychiatrist, says. "He discovered too late that he was in the wrong kind of work with the wrong type of wife. A job that does not give a man the satisfaction of achievement kills his incentive and becomes drudgery. A good salary will temper his frustration for a while, but if his wife is a domineering, waspish woman who continually reminds him that her father's business is supporting them in better style than he could provide on his own, he may make sex the instrument of his resentment. He will withhold himself from his wife or chase other women to punish her.

"This pattern is so common today that some far-fetched theories have been advanced to account for its sudden frequency. Men always have worked for relatives, the argument goes, so there must be a new, unexplained factor that is turning them against their wives in middle age. I think the answer is obvious. The sustained economic boom since World War Two has greatly increased the number of men who have been pulled to prosperity on the coattails of their fathers-in-law. Formerly, a high percentage of such businesses failed or did not make big money, and fewer husbands were beholden to wives' families for their financial security.

"Let me cite a typical example that can apply, with minor variations, to thousands of men. A new patient, forty-eight years old, came to me shortly after an operation for a disorder that was suspiciously psychosomatic. He tacitly admitted that he was seeing me at the insistence of his wife. They had not slept together for about six months. In my first session with him, he mentioned several times that he had been a good athlete and 'very popular' in school. He married the only child of a wealthy dress manufacturer in 1946 after four years in the Army and went to work for her father, but he hated it. Production details bored him, and he felt that making dresses was a reflection on his virility, a revealing clue that he had some doubts about it himself. He probably would have been happier had he gone out and met people as a salesman, but his father-in-law was grooming him to manage the business and wanted him to stay in the plant. Although the husband's antipathy for his work was a source of friction with his wife, their sexual activity was fairly regular until his father-in-law died and he tried to run the company.

"He made such a botch of things that the firm would have gone bankrupt if his wife had not stepped in. She was an aggressive woman and began to harp on his failure in contrast to her father's success. He was the nominal boss, but she made all the decisions, and everyone in the trade knew it. Their intercourse stopped when she took charge of the business. Having been emasculated by her in the office, he was unable to function as a male in bed.

"On his sixth visit to me, he blurted out his pent-up resentment of his wife and his feeling of guilt for failing to assert himself. That was the last I saw of him. His wife phoned before the next appointment and said he needed an operation for ulcers. His medical record showed no previous symptoms of such trouble. He was falling back again on a psychosomatic ailment as an excuse for his sexual inadequacy. He didn't want to regain his potency. Poor health was his weapon to make his wife suffer for demeaning him as a man."

Impotence and frigidity, the counterpart in women, may assume disguises that are not recognized readily. Everyone with a fairly wide circle of acquaintances knows couples whose marriages are running battles marked by rancor and tension. The relationships are utterly devoid of affection or even ordinary civility; the combatants seem to derive a perverse pleasure from humiliating each other publicly. Their animosity is so deep-rooted that it is difficult to imagine them calling truces periodically for sexual union, but they generally are more faithful than other couples with much less provocation for philandering.

A new insight to these unhappy unions was introduced by Dr. Paul H. Dince at a symposium on marriage problems sponsored by the Society of Medical Psychoanalysts in 1965. Dr. Dince found that in many disturbed marriages there is a recurring cycle he calls a "sexual refractory period," lasting from ten days to two weeks, in which intercourse is followed by avoidance of sex by one or both partners. "This pattern is based upon conflict and anxiety related to genital function and genital pleasure," Dr. Dince reported. "The anxiety often is rationalized in the form of derogatory attitudes toward the partner who, by this mechanism, is made the scapegoat for the individual's distress.

"Some women are threatened by a husband's sexual disinterest or impotence, because it represents to them a potential abandonment. Sexually frigid themselves, they require occasional sexual activity as proof of the husband's commitment. There are husbands whose need for sexual activity is very intense, not on the level of sensual gratification per se, but to restore continually wilting confidence in their masculinity or to reassure themselves that their wives will not become sexually interested in other men. Others, with similar underlying pathology, fear the sexual demands of their wives, for they are thereby exposed as sexually inadequate."

Couples who appear to be badly mismated actually may be held together by their offsetting emotional immaturity and personality defects, which would lead to divorce with other spouses. In the long run they probably reach a better sexual adjustment than either could make with another partner. Impotence and frigidity, although strange bedfellows, can share the same bed. A few minutes of intimacy, if only every ten days or two weeks, are better than none at all.

Case histories of a man and a woman were reviewed by Dr. Dince to illustrate the refractory cycle. The woman, after ten years of marriage and three children, was unable to respond regularly to her husband. In her background there was a strong sense of fear and guilt connected with adolescent masturbation and attachment to her father. "Orgasm posed a considerable threat to her for it was an experience which deprived her of her overvalued control," Dr. Dince commented. After intercourse, she avoided her husband and was angered by his advances. She became compulsive about household tasks, which kept her busy until late at night and exhausted her. She found excuses to retire later than her husband and complained of headaches. She berated herself for being a poor wife, but rationalized it on the grounds of her husband's offensive behavior. Her hostility gradually subsided toward the end of a two-week cycle; she had intercourse and then took refuge in another refractory period.

A man who went through a similar pattern had vague feelings of guilt and shame after intercourse, as though he had done something indecent to his wife. He was worried about his masculinity and, just before planning an approach to his wife, he derogated her in his fantasies, focusing on her shortcomings. He worked himself into such a rage that he provoked an argument with her, thereby avoiding a sexual encounter. Dr. Dince explained that the combination of rage and withdrawal is a typical defense mechanism to ward off sexual anxiety.

A highly revealing sign that a man past forty is drifting into self-induced impotence is persistent complaints of ailments that are not confirmed by medical examination. The hypochondriac's morbid concern for his health springs from a neurotic fear of death that suddenly may assume terrifying imminence in middle age. The sex drive, the supreme expression of the life force, conversely is a gauge of aging to a man who attaches undue importance to his declining score in the numbers game and interprets it as an omen of approaching impotence. Unlike a woman, who first sees evidence of time's passage in the mirror, a man cannot cheat the calendar with the cosmetic arts. He must invent a buffer for his ego. A face-saving explanation for his dwindling sexual activity is to attribute it to poor health—a stroke of bad luck for which he cannot be held accountable and is no reflection on his virility. The Don Juan type, who fancies himself a lady-killer, derives a peculiar satisfaction from imputing his disability to sexual excesses in his youth. A man has just so many arrows in his quiver, he reasons. If he was profligate with them as a young man and shot indiscriminately at targets of opportunity, he must pay for his folly now, but it was great fun while it lasted.

The utterly specious notion that frequent copulation is injurious to health is one of the hoariest myths in the folklore of sex. Even Aristotle gave it scientific credence and advised men to defer marriage until they were thirty-seven years old so that they and their wives would lose their reproductive powers and passions at approximately the same time. "It conduces the temperament not to marry too soon; for women who marry early are apt to be wanton; and in men too the bodily frame is stunted if they marry while they are growing," Aristotle wrote.

An old French proverb, "Each time we love, a bit of us must die," has helped to perpetuate the myth. The original meaning, that love is nurtured by sacrifices, has been garbled by superstition and religious fanaticism. A typical example came up in June, 1966, when Dr. J. K. Burns, an Irish professor of physiology at University College in Galway, declared that sex for pleasure alone causes cancer, a host of other serious diseases and results in deformed children. "It is well known medically," Dr. Burns said with mendacious glibness, "that overindulgence in the reproductive process, associated with overactivity of the germ-forming organs, leads to the formation of more and more abnormal cells which, in turn, cause the development of abnormal individuals." Dr. Burns added that he felt compelled to issue this warning, because the strict birth control policy of the Catholic Church appeared to be "wavering." Leading Irish gynecologists challenged Dr. Burns to produce the research supporting his contention, but he retreated into the gloomy seclusion of his medieval mind.

Once a man commences to fall back on failing health as an excuse for withdrawing from sex and says to himself, "I must not copulate, because it's bad for me," the will to impotence tightens its grip on him. "I must not copulate" soon becomes "I cannot copulate." To resolve all doubts, it can be stated unequivocally that regular sexual activity is not debilitating and holds absolutely no danger to health, even for people who have had severe coronary attacks. Remote-control measurements of the heart rates of men of all ages during coitus have shown that the exertion is equivalent to taking a brisk walk down the street. The idea that the strain on the heart is prohibitively high during intercourse is a complete fallacy.

A special group of men who have been driven to impotence by shame or despair merits sympathetic attention. They are sterile, unable to father children. Sterility and impotence are confused so frequently that it may be helpful to explain briefly the difference between the two conditions. An impotent man's reproductive capacity may be very high, but he lacks the ability—or desire—to produce an erection necessary to deliver the spermatozoa that fertilize the female's ovum. The sterile man is fully capable of gratifying a woman in intercourse, but his ejaculate lacks a sufficient number of sperm cells to impregnate her.

Until the organic causes of sterility are known, it must be suffered as a cruel, capricious misfortune that strikes many men. The fertile man's ejaculate normally contains between 90 and 110 million sperm cells. Theoretically, only one is needed to fertilize the ovum, but the enormous surplus is nature's way of assuring the propagation of the species. Another vital factor is the motility of the spermatozoa, or the ability to proceed from the testicles, where they are manufactured continuously, to the female's genital tract, a process that takes nearly three weeks. It is entirely possible for a man with less than 90 million sperm cells to beget a child, but when the count drops to 20 million it is a lost cause.

Estimates of male infertility in the United States and other Western countries range from 5 to 10 percent of the population. However, a ranking authority in the field, Dr. John MacLeod, of the Cornell University Medical School, believes the true figure is closer to 15 percent and climbing steadily. Dr. MacLeod concedes that the trend to early marriages combined with prosperity is bringing to the attention of physicians more men who want, but are unable to have, children. He is convinced, however, that a more important factor is contributing to the problem.

"I think the emotional pressures in our society are playing a very significant role in the rising incidence of male infertility," he says. "Doctors have long recognized that when a woman is upset, her menstrual cycle is disturbed, but we're just beginning to understand that the male's procreative process is equally sensitive to his environment. I've studied the potential fertility of about one thousand inmates of prisons and found it much higher than the average for the general population. The reason is obvious. Although prisoners are not exposed to the erotic stimulation that helps to maintain fertility, they are living in a protected, routinized milieu with no competitive economic pressures.

"One married couple in every eight has no children in the United States. Until a few years ago it was generally assumed that the wife's sterility was the cause of childless unions, but accurate tests indicate that the difficulty stems from the husband's deficient sperm count in 40 percent of the cases.

"It is a hellish blow to a man's pride to be told that he is incapable of begetting children. The one comforting thing in the depressing job of telling a couple who want children that they cannot have them is the touching reaction of the wife. She usually gets the report first, because the husband never suspects he is sterile. 'Please let me break it to him gently,' she invariably says. 'It's going to be an awful shock to him, and it will be better if we're alone.' If tactless people later ask why they don't have children, the wife always protects her husband by intimating that the trouble lies with her.

"Whenever possible, I try to see male patients after they have received the bad news to assure them that there is absolutely no correlation between the sperm count and virility. They can enjoy an active, satisfactory sex life indefinitely like normal men, but I'm afraid they don't believe me. Many lose

interest in intercourse, because they regard themselves as castrates and are ashamed of their deficiency. They soon become
impotent and compound their unhappiness.

"If a glimmer of hope could be given these men, countless
personal tragedies could be averted, but when they ask the
inevitable question, I'm forced to tell them that the results of
treatment have been most disappointing. Injections of testosterone to increase the sperm count rarely succeed. Surgery
may help when the ducts carrying the sperm from the testes
to the urethra [the outlet canal in the penis] are obstructed,
but such cases are rare. The harsh truth is that all known
therapy has failed for the overwhelming majority of men who
are sterile."

The prognosis for curing impotence is infinitely better. Dr.
Smiley Blanton, a veteran psychiatrist, declared that "only
about 10 percent of people with emotional problems need the
deep probing known as psychoanalysis. For the other 90 percent, intelligent self-analysis is sufficient." This ratio is particularly relevant to impotence, for most of its causes can be
cleared up with a cogent explanation—if the patient really
wants to regain his sexual powers.

The most difficult type of impotence to treat is rooted in the
Oedipal guilt described earlier. A man married to a woman
who unconsciously represents his mother, for whom he had an
erotic attachment in childhood, may be able to function sexually with his wife only if he is punished or humiliated for
violating the incest taboo. The frigid woman is dominated by
similar restraints. Dr. Karl A. Menninger told of a woman
who avoided intercourse with her husband, because a mental
image of her father's stern, disapproving face always appeared
before her during coitus.

"This woman and her husband themselves discovered that if
he would first strike her as if in anger she could then enjoy
intercourse normally," Dr. Menninger reported. "It is quite
clear, I think, that this woman had the feeling so many chil-

dren do that punishment squares everything, and that one punishment will do as well (or better than) another. Therefore she could dispel the frowning face of her father by carrying out the punishment which she felt she deserved for indulging in the act of sex which he disapproved.

"Precisely the same thing holds true of men. Indeed, it is this need for punishment which explains the favorable results sometimes obtained by painful treatment administered to the genital organs by urologists, in spite of the fact that rarely, if ever, is impotence dependent upon structural pathology."

An emotional cripple can be as potent as a prize stud with a prostitute, but his libido is paralyzed with a woman he respects, because he regards sex as degrading. Intercourse with a woman who is his social equal is tantamount to defiling a surrogate mother. This so-called Madonna complex is most prevalent in upper intellectual and cultural levels, leading skeptics who reject Freud to the caustic observation that sexual problems increase in direct ratio to the bankrolls of patients who can afford to pay a psychiatrist's fee. It is true, of course, that affluent people comprise the bulk of a psychiatrist's private practice, but the principle of the Madonna complex is exploited in brothels that cater to a lower-class clientele.

Cheap Southern bawdyhouses often have Negro girls in attendance for white customers who want them. Chinese girls waiting to be smuggled into the United States always can get space in Latin American crib joints, and their supposed anatomical peculiarity has nothing to do with their popularity. Brothels for French working men traditionally have drawn on North Africa for illiterate native girls. Elsewhere in Europe procurers prefer peasant girls to more sophisticated candidates from large cities. Prostitutes in cheap dives are not noted for their attractiveness or even for their proficiency in the arts of love. They are chosen deliberately for the bovine dimwittedness that gives the patron the needed feeling of superiority.

An interesting explanation for the high incidence of impo-

tence in the upper brackets of the social scale is advanced by
Dr. Kenneth Walker and Peter Fletcher in *Sex and Society:*
"In a certain stratum of English society it is considered 'good
form' to maintain a rigidly correct, polite demeanor under all
provocations. Neither excitement nor disgust, anger nor fear,
enjoyment nor boredom must be allowed unrestrained expression; and in some public schools training is carefully directed
to ensure that the finished product is capable of keeping 'a stiff
upper lip' through every crisis and is ready, like an officer of
the Guards, to 'die with his boots on.'

"It is no coincidence that among people so conditioned one
of the commonest sexual disorders is functional impotence
appearing only on marriage to a member of the same social
group. In an association with a prostitute or with a girl of an
'inferior' social class a young man may have no difficulty, but
he finds it impossible to 'let himself go' with a partner who
stands as a symbol of all the values from which he derives his
sense of personal dignity and self-confidence.

"So ingrained does the habit of reticence become in people
so educated that they sometimes have great difficulty in ac-
knowledging their need of help when they seek it at the hands
of a physician, irrespective of the kind of illness from which
they are suffering. It is not uncommon for them to apologize
for troubling the doctor with a description of their symptoms
and even when they are in serious physical pain or distress of
mind they may maintain an air of stoical unconcern so successfully that the doctor must exercise all his trained powers of
observation to 'read between the lines' of their self-control and
so arrive at a true diagnosis of their condition."

The dread of impotence always has made otherwise intelligent men easy marks for phony cure-alls peddled by charlatans. Some of the eccentrics were reputable scientists who,
seeking to relieve their own anxieties, went off the deep end
convinced that they were on the verge of a breakthrough in
the quest for rejuvenation. There is absolutely no nostrum,

drug, device, therapy or food that will effect a permanent improvement in a man's potency. All such panaceas are an utter waste of money and may lead to disappointments that compound the basic trouble. Yet believers, like hope, spring eternal.

Every year the Food and Drug Administration seizes thousands of fraudulent, high-priced contraptions guaranteed to restore sexual vigor. A large room in the F.D.A.'s headquarters in Washington is filled with machines bought by gullible people to counteract impotence with mild electric shocks, ultraviolet and infrared rays, massages and even music. One of the prize exhibits in this museum of quackery is the Orgone Box, a creation of the late Dr. Wilhelm Reich, a disciple of Freud who became a classic prototype of the mad professor. He was convicted of fraud in 1954 and put away in protective custody. The Orgone Box was simply a wooden crate lined with sheet metal that was supposed to act as a powerful sex stimulant by concentrating on a man huddled inside it the cosmic and physical forces that, according to Reich, produced orgasms.

Variations on the theme were firmly rooted in superstition before history was first recorded. The Old Testament relates that King David was advised to inhale the breath of young virgins to recapture his youthful powers. He took Abishag the Shunammite to his bed with distressing results, for "he knew her not" and died shortly thereafter. Ancient Syrians and Hebrews bathed in and drank the blood of youths and maidens. Roman aristocrats vied in leaping into the arena to suck the blood of fallen gladiators. Paracelsus, a famous medieval physician turned alchemist, claimed he had discovered a secret elixir but died at forty-eight before he could bequeath it to posterity. Cagliostro, a notorious Renaissance swindler, carried on a thriving racket selling a philter, concocted from sandalwood, senna and dill, that was reputed to have made him a formidable womanizer at a "vast" age. He died at fifty-two. Pope Innocent VIII immediately succumbed in 1492 to a blood transfusion from three young men, a popular remedy for longevity.

The search took a more scientific turn late in the nineteenth century. Dr. Charles Brown-Séquard, an eminent physiologist then seventy-two, introduced a new technique for prolonging life and potency by injecting himself with an extract of dogs' testicles. He survived it for five years. Dr. Serge Voronoff made headlines throughout the world a half-century ago by grafting testicles from monkeys on aging men, but later reports testified that the experiments were hollow failures.

The Russians always have been fascinated by rejuvenation. Dr. Élie Metchnikoff, deputy director of the prestigious Pasteur Institute, recommended yogurt. Dr. Alexander Bogomolets, his assistant, claimed ACS, a serum he had discovered, did the trick. As recently as 1957 Dr. Anna Aslan, a Rumanian, created a stir with something she called "novocain therapy." As Robert DeRopp, a biochemist, observes, Russian experiments seem to achieve favorable results only behind the Iron Curtain. Efforts to uncover the secret of longevity are not confined to Russia, however. Dr. Paul Niehans, a Swiss, was appointed to the Pontifical Academy of Sciences, presumably for the benefits derived by Pope Pius XII after World War II from injections of cells taken from unborn lambs.

The latest treatment palmed off as legitimate medical therapy for increasing sexual vigor is an injection of hormones at fees ranging up to $50 a shot. Small doses of testosterone to correct a deficiency of sex hormones, a natural accompaniment of aging in men and women after fifty, often effect an improvement in a patient's general physical tone which, incidentally, promotes sexual desire. There is no evidence, however, that testosterone or any other synthetic hormone is a direct booster of potency. If it does seem to stimulate the libido, it is purely a psychological reaction—the "will to impotence" in reverse. The man wants to believe he is capable of coitus and regains his confidence. Injections of placebo have produced the same results as testosterone.

Men are so eager to grasp at any straw promising revital-
ized potency that reputable medical publications accept
papers based on data that ordinarily would be rejected sum-
marily as inconclusive or unscientific. A prime example was
an article in the December, 1964, issue of the *Journal of the
American Geriatric Society* written by Dr. Miley B. Wesson, a
practicing urologist in San Francisco for fifty-four years. He
asserted that his findings were supported by records kept on
7379 patients.

"Testosterone used in adequate dosage over a long period
of time can result in striking, even 'miraculous,' improvement
in muscle tone and the general sense of well-being," he wrote.
"It can act as a tonic, making old men 'young' and young men
more vigorous sexually." Dr. Wesson claimed that an eighty-
three-year-old man had "a much larger penis and more frequent erections" after taking testosterone and declared it had
even cured a few patients who were "believed" to be sterile. A
screening committee has yet to consider Dr. Wesson a candidate for the Nobel Prize in medicine.

A good deal of preposterous advice has been advanced by
alleged authorities for correcting premature ejaculation, an
early indication of impotence. A technical discussion of the
subject in the October 15, 1965, issue of the *New York State
Journal of Medicine* wound up suggesting that orgasms can be
retarded by "tightening the anal sphincter during coitus, curl-
ing the toes or pinching the skin and using a condom to reduce
the stimulation of vaginal friction." Above all, male readers
were solemnly exhorted to "occupy the mind with nonsexual
thoughts." Nutrition experts may next assure famine-stricken
populations that the pangs of hunger can be assuaged by con-
templating the spendors of nature.

A word on aphrodisiacs: Nonsense. The naive belief that
certain foods increase potency is older than artifacts from the
Iron Age. The ancients favored onions, eggs, fish and honey.
The Romans called tomatoes "love apples." The spices of
China and India, highly prized during the Middle Ages for

love potions, helped to make rancid meat and fish edible, but they did nothing for the sexual appetite. The fancy prices paid today for oysters, caviar and asparagus are sustained partly by the sexual powers attributed to them. There is still a brisk demand for Spanish fly, a powder made from the blister beetle, and yohimbine, a substance from the bark of a South African tree. Both preparations are not only worthless but cause dangerous inflammation of the genitourinary tract and can be fatal if taken in large quantities.

The best—and only genuine—aphrodisiac is frequent intercourse. Like any other physical process, the pattern of sexual response becomes sluggish and deteriorates with disuse. Regular stimulation of the intricate network of impulses in copulation firms up the tone of the reflex chain in exactly the same way that running a car charges the battery and tunes up the engine.

"A common cause of premature ejaculation is the fallacy of 'saving up' for a good, strong orgasm," Dr. John MacLeod says. "The testes do not regulate their activity according to the demand made on them. They work like a clock, continually manufacturing sperm cells. If stale cells are not discharged fairly frequently in orgasms, they clog up the genitourinary system and literally spill over after a long layoff from intercourse. Krafft-Ebing is best known for his research in sexual aberrations, but he was a first-rate neurologist too. He concluded that abstinence leads to more male sexual problems than debauchery, and a lot of us in the profession are inclined to agree with him."

Coitus is increasingly important for the morale of a man past forty. The rat race drains him of psychic vitality for which the prime source of replenishment is the exhilaration of sex. As he grows older, oppressed by real and imagined aches, doubts and anxieties, regular intercourse gives him assurance that he still is capable of functioning as the compleat male. If he only knew that half the battle already is won. . . .

# 9

## On Female Sexuality

***

WHEN A YOUNG MAN BEGINS HIS TENTATIVE EXPLORATION OF sex, he invariably is astonished to discover that women are easy conquests—a reaction he never completely shakes off regardless of his later experience and sophistication. He will deny it, of course, but in middle age he still is startled by a woman's uninhibited enjoyment of intercourse when she is aroused erotically, and he is enormously flattered if an attractive female responds to his advances. Instead of delighting in their good fortune, however, many men feel threatened by women's passion in coitus and often retreat from it in confusion.

We smile indulgently at such relics of hidebound prudishness as the statement made in 1875 by Dr. William Acton, the leading gynecologist in London, who declared that it was "a vile aspersion of women" to say they were stirred by sexual desire. Only "lascivious" females, he asserted, derived any pleasure from submitting to man's carnal appetite. Today, we speak glibly of woman's emancipation and profess to recognize intellectually her right to equality of gratification in bed, but our enlightened attitude is strictly a pose. It still is unacceptable in our society for a wife to have a stronger sex drive than her husband.

All the sexual mores of Western culture are geared to the assumption that a man has a more imperative and constant need for intercourse than a woman. He sets the pace for the frequency of coitus in marriage, and a wife must defer to it or run the risk of social condemnation. Censure of a man's philandering is tempered by speculation that he might have been driven to an illicit affair by his wife's apathy in bed. A woman is branded a tramp, with no mitigating excuse, if she strays afield seeking the sexual gratification she does not get from her husband. The restraints on a woman, although necessary for stabilized family relationships, conflict head-on with the biological fact that she is capable of much more sexual activity than one man possibly can provide.

Anatomically, a woman always is ready for intercourse, whether or not she is in a receptive mood for it. The result is much more satisfactory, to be sure, when she is eager to receive her lover and her ardor has been intensified in foreplay, but neither condition is essential for her participation in coitus. Further, her capacity for multiple orgasms is not severely limited, like a man's, by the depletion of seminal fluid in an ejaculation. Under clinical test conditions, it is not unusual for a woman to have a half-dozen orgasms within a half-hour. Before a man can initiate copulation his nervous system must be functioning at top efficiency to produce an erection and, as we have seen, it is far from an automatic reaction even under the most favorable opportunities.

There is no question that women, liberated from the straitjacket of repression, are more aggressive in demanding sexual satisfaction and are putting virility to a sterner test today than a generation ago. It should be a wonderful tonic to men. The challenge of gratifying a woman in full bloom certainly is more stimulating and healthier for a middle-aged man than slipping listlessly into sexual senescence. Ben Franklin, whose restless curiosity took him into more boudoirs than school books care to admit, said it all in his famous essay on choosing a mistress. He advised men to seek older women "because they are so grateful!!"

Much of the stultifying claptrap that surrounds sex stems from the same nonsense that clutters up football. Sideline coaches have taken the fun and spontaneity out of a rousing physical performance by turning the participants into symbols that move in mysterious ways known only to the masterminds. The football coach's tedious X's and O's on diagrams of formations correspond to the esoteric labels pinned on people in technical journals straining for angles that make catchy newspaper headlines. A typical example of this sort of thing was an article on "The Clitorid Woman" by Dr. Thomas J. Meyers, of Los Angeles, in the April, 1966, issue of *The Psychiatric Quarterly*.

According to Dr. Meyers, men and women can be divided into two sexual prototypes. A man is a seminal or a penile; a woman is a uterine or a clitorid. Seminals and uterines are clods insensitive to the ecstasy of sex. Peniles and clitorids—terms derived from the principal sex organs—are the elite of the earth; they are infused with "an intangible aura of sex." "A woman of the clitorid type loves a man for his own sake," Dr. Meyers rhapsodized. "From her first love onward, she knows no greater satisfaction than sexual enjoyment, i.e., 'love' as it is called. She seeks and attracts the attention of males and arrives at an understanding with them with the help of a glance or a gesture, is ready to play her part in sexual intrigue and is the first to reach the stage of sexual abandon."

And how does one recognize these ineffably alluring creatures? Well, sir, a clitorid walks "with a hip-swinging movement" and "a sexually alive pelvis" that apparently has the thrust of a cruiser under full steam. Dr. Meyers' description evokes fond memories of Mae West sashaying in her parodies of a *femme fatale* that convulsed movie audiences thirty-five years ago.

Sexuality is not a component that can be isolated and analyzed under a microscope like a blood sample. It is the sum of an individual's entire personality, his experiences and, especially, his culture. The economic pressures generated by the current social climate are a constant drain on the male libido, yet a middle-aged man who has been a capable performer and is now uncertain of his virility may be partly to blame for his own predicament. Psychotherapists who are familiar with the symptoms agree with Dr. Milton R. Sapirstein that many men, intimidated by women's greater sexual potential, subconsciously prefer wives who are frigid or have a low level of erotic responsiveness. "If he wakes the sleeping giantess, she may prove too much for him," Dr. Sapirstein explains. "Asleep or somnolent, on the other hand, she is no threat."

There is fascinating evidence that primitive man also recognized and feared woman's stronger sex drive. Classical myths, founded in some measure on historical fact and reflecting widely held beliefs, clearly indicate that women were considered superior to men. Throughout Asia Minor and cultures bordering on the Mediterranean, the early social systems were matriarchies in which descent was traced from the mother and property was inherited by daughters.

"Ancient Europe had no gods," Robert Graves wrote in *The Greek Myths.* "The Great Goddess was regarded as immortal, changeless and omnipotent; and the concept of fatherhood had not yet been introduced into religious thought. She took lovers, but for pleasure, not to provide her children with a father. Men feared, adored and obeyed the matriarch; the hearth which she tended in a cave or a hut being their earliest social center, and motherhood was their prime mystery. Thus, the first victim of a Greek public sacrifice [a handsome youth] was always offered to Hestia of the Hearth. . . . In this archaic religious system there were, as yet, neither gods nor priests, but only a universal goddess and her priestesses, woman being the dominant sex and man her frightened victim."

Frequent references are found in Greek legends to the Maenads, described as madwomen who staged wild, orgiastic fertility rites. The revels degenerated into such fierce conflicts that men recruited for the celebrations sometimes were literally torn apart by women fighting for their sexual services. Pain was inflicted and suffered stoically, but men were extraordinarily kind to women during pregnancy. Childbearing was considered a divine gift, and men were awed that women alone were the recipients of it, for they had no comprehension of their own role in procreation.

During the nine months that elapsed between conception and the delivery of a baby, a woman copulated with so many partners that a physical function which seemed as natural as urinating was not associated with the miracle of birth. Prehistoric people ruled by superstition attributed pregnancy to such supernatural phenomena as a celestial wind or a magic bean that took seed in a woman's stomach. She began to lose her superior status when man discovered he could beget many children, who were essential to the future security of the tribe, while she was producing only one.

The giantess was put in protective custody, but the wardens carefully avoided antagonizing her by making the bonds too repressive. The Hebrews, whose stern moral precepts laid down in the Ten Commandments subsequently were incorporated into most religious codes, were remarkably permissive in their attitude toward sex—and not to accommodate the master of the house.

"It is interesting to note that Jewish tradition has always given full recognition to the sexuality of women," Rabbi Samuel Glasner, of Baltimore, explains in *The Encyclopedia of Sexual Behavior*. "In fact, there has been a tendency from the Bible down through the later Jewish literature to regard the sexual drive in woman as greater, and more constant and aggressive than that in man. One frequently finds it asserted that it is women who lead men into sexual misconduct. One provision in the Talmud, for instance, would permit a woman to be alone with two men but would prohibit a man from being alone with two women."

A stalwart son was the greatest blessing God could bestow

on a devout follower of Judiasm. "In several places the
Talmud offers as a prescription for the begetting of sons the
suggestion that the husband might earn this much-coveted reward by seeing to it that his wife was fully satisfied in intercourse before he himself reached his own climax. Said one of
the rabbis, 'Any man whose wife asks him for sexual relations
will have sons like whom there were none ever before!' "

The Talmud contained specific provisions for satisfying a
woman's sexual desire. A husband was advised to have intercourse with her before leaving on a journey and immediately
upon his return. One reason the ancient Hebrews sanctioned
polygamy was that it absorbed the surplus of women resulting
from the higher mortality of men in war and the hazards of
daily life. They recognized that sexually deprived women
could be disruptive elements in a community by enticing husbands and unmarried males into mischief. When a man died
leaving a widow, a brother or a close male relative was obliged
to marry her, both to support her and satisfy her sexual needs.
In the Old Testament there are numerous accounts of women
who took the initiative in sexual misdemeanors. Lot's daughters got him drunk and lured him to an incestuous bed to have
children by him. Potiphar's wife seduced Joseph, and Rachel
and Leah bargained for the sexual favors of Jacob, their husband. The forbidden fruit Eve offered Adam was construed by
some Biblical scholars as symbolic of the eternal temptation of
women.

Christian morality was tolerant of sexual pleasure until ex-
tremists assailed it as the instrument of man's Fall, but threats
of hellfire and damnation for sinners did not intimidate
women at the height of the Church's influence during the
Middle Ages. Pious Heloise, the paragon of feminine virtue,
wrote Abelard: "However sacred and honest the word wife
may be for you, for me it always sounds delightful to be called
your sweetheart or even your whore." The ribald tales of
Chaucer and Boccaccio, which depicted women as willing

accomplices in illicit sex, were enormously popular, because they were authentic commentaries on contemporary manners. The sensuality of women was a central theme in Renaissance art and literature. Ladies of quality participated as lustily as common wenches in the debauchery of Restoration England and France under the Bourbons.

The notion that sex was offensive to refined women was an invention of the nineteenth century. Standards of behavior, like fashions in clothes, originate with the upper class, then filter down through the social order. The starchy moral code of Queen Victoria, who barred from her court divorcees and women remotely linked with scandal, was adopted by the parvenus of the manufacturing class, acutely self-conscious of their lack of social graces. Victoria constantly delivered lectures on decorum to her relatives, who occupied most of the thrones of Europe, but the agitation for political reform that swept the continent in the middle of the century was a more effective curb on the freewheeling aristocracy. Sensuality went underground, and rectitude supplanted sophistication as the entrée to high society. Actually, the suffocating prudery of the Victorian Age lasted little more than one generation. In the 1890's women began to stir restively against restraints, and when they kicked over the traces after World War I the so-called sexual revolution was, in effect, a reversion to the earlier, freer expression of female sexuality.

Although feminists hailed the Emancipation, not everyone has been happy with the trend in women's sexual attitudes since the 1920's. One critical opinion that touched off wide debate was a lengthy paper by Dr. Mary Jane Sherfey in the January, 1966, issue of the *Journal of the American Psychoanalytic Association*. Dr. Sherfey, who has done extensive research on the evolution of sexuality, later discussed the central theme of her article in an interview.

"Women have read and heard so much about sexual equality that they often are overly aggressive in demanding it," she

said. "They want instant gratification, and they have no patience with men who do not give it to them. Just last week two
new male patients who have been married less than three
months came to me with identical problems. Both are ejaculating prematurely during intercourse, and their wives have told
them flatly they will get divorces if the trouble is not corrected
quickly.

"The men are in their early twenties and usually have a
second, slower orgasm that brings their wives to a climax, but
the girls feel that their husbands are short-changing them by
going off without them the first time. I have told the wives that
it may take several months before the emotional complications
that are causing the premature ejaculations can be cleared up,
but I'm afraid they will not wait until the treatment is completed. They will pack up and leave if they don't see immediate results.

"The disturbing thing about the reactions of both wives is
that they were not surprised or even disappointed by their
husbands' sexual inadequacy. It's almost as if they had bought
a ticket in a lottery knowing they had a slim chance of draw-
ing a winning number. In recent years a steady procession of
women have told me, 'My husband is a lousy lover, but what
can you expect from men nowadays?' It's dangerous to make
generalizations on the basis of patients' complaints, which
may not be valid. An analyst's impressions can be distorted by
seeing only people with special problems. It seems to me,
though, that women are developing a hostile, almost contemptuous, attitude toward men as sexual partners, and it's
going to lead to social chaos unless some sense is drummed
into them.

"We must recognize that women possess a much stronger
sexual drive than men and that a line must be drawn between
liberty and license. The need for such a clear-cut distinction—
and I'm not thinking primarily of the moral issue—is more
imperative than ever, because the lifting of traditional re-

straints and the improvement in contraceptives have brought a profound change in female sexual behavior. Reports that the contraceptive pill is promoting promiscuity among unmarried girls are not exaggerations. The girls—and a lot of mature women who should know better—are discounting the enduring value of love in marriage and are looking for quick physical gratification. I shudder to think what will happen in another ten or fifteen years, when an entire generation of women brought up on the pill begins to make inordinate sexual demands middle-aged husbands cannot satisfy.

"One thing is inevitable if the present trend continues. A return to enforced suppression of the female sexual drive will be mandatory if women do not control it themselves. Otherwise, the family as a biological unit will disappear, and the entire structure of adult and child relationships will collapse."

There is a better remedy for the crisis Dr. Sherfey envisions, and it is a splendid prescription even if the crisis does not materialize. Booster shots of potency cannot be pumped into a man past forty like injections of vitamins, and he does not need them if he is reasonably healthy and vigorous. His sexual potential is adequate to satisfy the normal requirements of a woman, but he does not always perform up to the full capability of it for two reasons. He fails to cultivate new, exciting erotic techniques or, worse yet, he still has sophomoric illusions about the sacrifices a woman makes when she goes to bed with him. She enjoys sex and wants it as much as he does, but there are men who practically grovel with gratitude when their wives grant them their conjugal rights with the sullen resignation that suggests the martyrdom of Edith Cavell. A man who permits his wife to use sex as an instrument of guilt or penance deserves what he gets.

Stendhal wrote that a cold, passionless woman has not yet met an accomplished lover. When boredom with repetitious methods of coitus are cited as a cause of declining interest in sex, the inference always is that husbands alone are the victims of it. Wives also rebel against the monotony of the marriage bed, especially in middle age when, having cast off their inhibitions, they are willing to experiment with innovations in the arts of love described in the next chapter. A woman with grown children usually has a lighter load of emotional pressures and household chores. She has more nervous and physical energy for intercourse, but she often is frustrated by her husband's apathy—or his prudishness.

Every woman who lives with a man discovers that his risqué talk and rakish capering are a camouflage for a puritanical streak that extends across his shoulder blades. He ogles other women wearing dresses cut below the sternum and bikinis that would be banned by the aborigines of New Guinea, but he objects strenuously when she exposes herself publicly. A man whose language would enrich a stevedore's vocabulary is embarrassed when his wife inadvertently uses a four-letter expletive in the presence of other people.

The classic reaction of a man who decides to marry a girl with whom he is having an affair is to propose that they stop further intercourse until the wedding. He rarely sticks to his straitlaced resolve, of course, but he reproaches himself for degrading his future wife, a thought that never enters her mind. Perhaps the strongest deterrent to infidelity is the pangs of conscience that assail a man after an extramarital fling. A prostitute always can spot a customer who does not use her type of service regularly. He insists on kissing her, as though that token of love will wipe out the taint of commercial sex.

A revealing, if somewhat exaggerated, difference between male and female sexual attitudes was found in the experiments at Washington University conducted by Dr. Masters and Mrs. Johnson. Members of the staff observed, took motion pictures and recorded on machines the physical reactions of men and women during coitus and masturbation. In the first twenty months, only male and female prostitutes were recruited, and paid, for the tests. "Availability was the determining factor during the initial stages of the program," Dr. Masters reported. "It was presumed, at that time, that study subjects from more conservative segments of the general population would not be available (a presumption which later proved to be entirely false)."

Dr. Masters had no trouble getting volunteers from University personnel. A total of 312 men and 382 women, ranging in age from eighteen to eighty-nine, participated in the tests. Among them were 276 married couples. More than 70 percent of the subjects had college or postgraduate training.

Most people are inclined to look askance at men and women who permit themselves to be observed during the most intimate of all human relationships, even for clinical research. This does not concern us. The pertinent point here is their response to the tests. An orientation period of three to six half-hour sessions was arranged to accustom the subjects to the presence of staff members, cameras and medical paraphernalia—and the women desensitized to the lack of privacy much faster and easier than the men. There were numerous failures by the subjects to go through with the tests. Men accounted for 65 percent of the washouts; they were unable to produce erections under the scrutiny of strangers. Once women accepted the ground rules, though, they were singularly unashamed to copulate in front of an audience.

"When women put aside the screen of modesty, they usually are more honest about their sexual needs than men," Dr. Theodor Reik says. Men rarely seek the advice of psychotherapists or marriage counselors for sexual problems unless their wives insist on it. Male self-esteem cannot tolerate the suspicion of deficient potency, much less confirmation of it. The chief exceptions to the rule are homosexuals who want justification of their deviation rather than treatment for it. Other men, when telling a physician of their sexual difficulties, resort to the transparent dodge of attributing their symptoms to a relative or a friend. Experienced practitioners go along with this evasion and discuss the problem impersonally, the only way a man will hold still for it.

Some consultants say women would be much happier if they had never heard of the orgasm, and it is not a facetious remark. The commonest complaint of wives who are dissatisfied sexually is that their husbands do not bring them to strong orgasms consistently. A woman's concern with reaching an acute climax every time she has intercourse corresponds to the male's obsession with the numbers game. The identical psychological and physical factors that depress a man's libido affect the intensity of a woman's erotic arousal. Further, her desire fluctuates sharply during her menstrual cycle—it usually is at the peak during the first two weeks—and continues to vary after the menopause. Yet many women think that anything short of an overwhelming orgasm detracts from their femininity, just as men fear that inability to get an erection spontaneously, regardless of the circumstances, denotes a loss of masculinity.

The climax to coitus has been depicted so extravagantly in literature and films that expectations have been aroused which are impossible for a woman to attain in every experience. D. H. Lawrence described the orgasm as "a final, massive and dark collision of the blood." Pilar, Hemingway's lusty gypsy in *For Whom the Bell Tolls,* asked Maria after she had spent the night with Robert Jordan, "Did the earth move?" In magazine fiction, orgasms have been likened to "the explosion of giant firecrackers," "the violent upheaval of a long dormant volcano" and "a blinding flash of agonizing rapture bursting into a thousand brilliant pinwheels in her brain." When thwarted movie lovers finally meet in a passionate clinch, the heavens erupt with thunder and lightning or turbulent waves dash against a rugged cliff. Maxine Davis pulled out all the stops in *The Sexual Responsibility of Woman:*

"This is it. This is the moment of ecstasy when a woman

soars along a Milky Way among stars all her own. This is the high mountain-top of love of which the poets sing. Her whole being is a full orchestra playing the fortissimo of a glorious symphony."

Now then. Many women are not transported to the stars by an orgasm, the earth does not move nor do they seethe with massive collisions. They may be exhilarated or have a delightful sensation of release, but they seldom are shaken to the cores of their souls in coitus. The intensity of an orgasm is governed by so many delicate, interacting influences that it varies continually in each individual. That should be obvious after a few experiences, but no one will ever know how many husbands have been afflicted with feelings of guilt or inadequacy by the unrealistic demands of women for maximum gratification every time they engage in intercourse. A marriage counselor tells of a bride of six months who was asked why she wanted a divorce. "I thought it would be like a countdown at Cape Kennedy whenever I slept with my husband," she answered. "My big hero didn't get me off the launching pad more than a couple of times each month."

The irony of such complaints is that even a woman with a strong sex drive who is thoroughly satisfied with her husband often is not certain whether she has had an orgasm. Since there is no tangible evidence like the male's ejaculate, it is entirely possible that she is not always aware of having reached a climax. It is not a profoundly stirring finale of a symphony, to be sure, but it can be as pleasurable as a favorite song. Marital relations embrace a wide scale of emotions ranging from an urgent biological need to a tender expression of affection. A woman who does not recognize this is immature or, more than likely, insecure of her femininity.

For the last forty years surveys have shown that about 10 percent of the married women in the United States and England never have had an orgasm during intercourse. Approximately the same ratio reach a climax so rarely that the incidence is negligible. Critics who dispute the statistics claim that they are weighted with young women who have not been married long enough to have established a definite pattern of response in coitus. This objection did not apply, however, to a study of couples married between sixteen and twenty years that was made by sociologists Alexander Clark and Paul Wallin in 1965. The poll of wives presumably at the peak of their erotism closely duplicated the findings for broader age groups.

"Perhaps as many as a fifth to a fourth of middle-class American wives never or infrequently have an orgasm in their marital relations," Clark and Wallin reported. Their conclusion hardly was a startling revelation: "Conditions for increasing the female's responsiveness are more apt to be met in marriages in which partners love each other and are concerned with the other's needs and happiness."

The formula for sexual compatability is not quite that uncomplicated. There is an old joke that well-mated people put on the best fights, because they are matched so evenly. Couples who battle constantly over money, children and other common causes of tension are often held together by a strong physical attraction, and, conversely, there are others who can be in rapport everywhere except in bed. Total orgastic failure in a mature woman with no organic disability invariably is an indication of frigidity, and no man can help her overcome it without the assistance of a psychotherapist. Nor can a loving, solicitous husband completely dispel another obstacle to sexual accord—the self-doubts implanted in a woman by an arbitrary Freudian principle that conflicts with the nature of her orgasms. Relatively very few wives have been in analysis, but every woman who has read a marriage manual or a book on marital relations has been exposed to Freud's theory, which, despite strong evidence that tends to disprove his hypothesis, is still staunchly supported by his disciples.

No aspect of female sexuality has been argued as vehemently as the question whether the center of a woman's arousal during an orgasm should be the clitoris or the vagina. The clitoris is a unique organ in that its sole purpose is to provide erotic sensation. The penis is not precisely homologous to the clitoris, because the male organ also has the important functions of delivering sperm to the ovum and serving as the outlet for the bladder.

Freud recognized that the clitoris is an adolescent girl's primary source of sexual excitement in masturbation and petting, but he stipulated that in the transition to womanhood this sensitivity must be transferred to the vagina for a "mature" orgasm in coitus. He did not explain how this shift can be effected so that the sensory reaction to an orgasm, which involves the entire nervous system, is localized in the vagina. Freud insisted, however, that a woman who is unable to achieve an orgasm solely through vaginal stimulation is immature psychosexually.

Pinpointing within a few inches the exact spot where an orgasm is felt could be dismissed as an academic quibble if not for a crucial point: Many women cannot reach an orgasm unless their partners massage the clitoral area by hand during coitus. Freud flatly asserted that such women are frigid. Some of his followers have gone further and assert that women who need clitoral manipulation have latent homosexual tendencies.

The damage done by these blanket indictments cannot be exaggerated. "There is an ever-growing incidence of guilt, fear and resentment in otherwise healthy women who find themselves unable to achieve the elusive prize of the vaginal orgasm," Dr. Sherfey declared in her article. The majority of the non-Freudian authorities in the field have repudiated the old concept, but few standard manuals read by women have been updated to incorporate new, highly significant data on female arousal during intercourse. Until the revisions are made, countless women will continue to be disturbed by nagging self-suspicions of frigidity or Lesbianism. The only transfer will be the shifting of blame to their husbands for failing to bring them to "mature" climaxes.

Since Freud was a meticulous scientist, he undoubtedly would have modified his theory to conform with later research. Kinsey contended that the vaginal orgasm was "a biologic impossibility," and although he was guilty of overstatement the evidence gathered in clinical tests strongly indicates that very few women can isolate vaginal responses in an orgasm from the reaction throughout the rest of the body. The vagina is devoid of nerve endings and is so insensitive that minor operations routinely are performed there without anesthesia. The gratification a woman derives from deep penetration by the male is purely psychic, a sense of unity with, and fulfillment by, her lover.

Professional opinion regarding clitoral manipulation has made such a complete turnabout that it now is recommended, especially for middle-aged couples. A woman must be stimulated continuously during coitus or the level of her arousal will drop instantaneously, even in the middle of an orgasm. A man past forty tends to have faster orgasms and is unable to maintain a strong erection for more than a few seconds after ejaculating. As a consequence, his partner is "hung up" and cannot reach a climax unless she is touched in the clitoral area—a practice that is far preferable to the feeling of frustration she will have without it.

The premise that a "normal" woman should reach an orgasm solely from the friction of the penis on her clitoris was based on a fallacy of female physiology. Such contact *never* is made when the male is atop his partner or lying beside her, because the clitoris is located about an inch and a half, sometimes farther, above the opening to the vagina. If a man tries to "ride high" on the clitoris, his downward thrusts press painfully on the entrance to the vagina. The favored position among the ancient Greeks was the woman astride the man— they called it "the horse of Hector"—because it enabled her to rub her clitoris against the shaft of the penis. Virtually all couples have experimented with this position as an exciting variation, but most women are vaguely disturbed that our mores do not approve of it.

Perhaps the most valuable result of the research by Dr. Masters was to settle, once and for all, the controversy over the vaginal vs. the clitoral orgasm. "From an anatomic point of view, there is absolutely no difference in the responses of the pelvic viscera to effective sexual stimulation, regardless of whether the stimulation occurs as a result of clitoral area manipulation, natural or artificial coition or, for that matter, breast manipulation alone," he concluded.

"It's hard to dispute the mass of evidence Masters has presented, but I suppose a majority of Freudian psychoanalysts will refuse to accept it," Dr. Sherfey comments. "The clitoral-vaginal transfer is such a key principle of Freud's theory that some sweeping revisions will have to be made before his school recognizes that it is perfectly normal for a woman to require clitoral manipulation to reach an orgasm. It's heresy in some quarters to say Freud was wrong, but the truth of the matter is that we're just beginning to get a better understanding of female sexuality."

Leave the abstruse questions to the pundits. A bed is not the place for intellectual exercises. A woman is to be loved, not understood.

# 10

# The Arts of Love

\* \* \*

*Think you if Laura had been Petrarch's wife*
*He would have written sonnets all his life?*
                                    *—Byron*

SPONTANEITY IS THE SPICE OF SEX IN MIDDLE AGE AND, CON-
trary to Byron's sardonic couplet, it can infuse marriage
with a full measure of erotic pleasure until physical infirmities
intervene. Byron's tragic death at thirty-six fighting for Greek
independence cast a romantic aura over his conquests, but he
made his reputation as a great lover the easy way. He left his
wife and child after a year and dashed through a series of
affairs, some of which a more discriminating man would not
have crossed the street, or a Venetian canal, to consummate.

Any lusty bumpkin with the same opportunities could have
matched Byron's box score. The genuine test of ardor is sustaining it with one partner. A husband and wife who still
arouse mutual excitement after three or four decades are more
proficient in the arts of love than the noisome "celebrities"
who infest gossip columns, bouncing from pillow to bedpost
with a parade of boudoir athletes. They usually wind up sleeping with rejects like themselves.

Variety may be the mother of enjoyment, as Disraeli said,

but spontaneity is the father of sexual gratification. The principal deterrent to marital intercourse in middle age is boredom with repeating the same routine under unchanging conditions as rigid as a railroad timetable. Marriage inevitably imposes fixed patterns on all habits, particularly sexual activity, and unless a conscious effort is made to break the monotony coitus can become as perfunctory as kissing a cousin.

Wives refuse to believe that husbands are looking for new erotic stimulation rather than new bedmates when they stray after many years of fidelity, but that is the basic reason in the great majority of cases. A man soon discovers, however, that spontaneity is more bracing than variety, for the different experiences he can find with another woman are limited. There is nothing new under the sun—or the sheets.

Every sexual technique known today was described in art and literature dating back to 2000 B.C. All the male and female erogenous zones that incite passion were classified with clinical precision in ancient Sanskrit manuscripts. The genital kiss, supposedly a French invention, was a common practice in the higher cultures of Asia and the Mediterranean before the first nomads pitched their tents on the present site of Paris; it also was prevalent among the Incas of Peru and the natives of Bali when European adventurers arrived. A typical comedy device in the satirical plays Aristophanes wrote 2400 years ago was the confusion of a jaded, middle-aged husband who was introduced to an unconventional position in coitus by a courtesan, then discovered that his wife was equally adept at it.

Although the diversion may not seem worth the complications it can bring, the chance to copulate at odd hours during the day is, for many men, the most intriguing aspect of an extramarital affair. Their revolt against the tedium of marriage centers on dissatisfaction that intercourse with their wives always occurs, like burglary, under the cover of darkness. From a purely practical viewpoint, the end of the evening is the least favorable time for sex in middle age. Physical energy is at the lowest ebb; the accumulated mental pressures of the day tend to throw a damper on the impulsive surges of desire that fine-tune the libido and keep it at a high pitch. This steady erosion of a man's sexuality induces a psychological fatigue that causes him to regard marital relations as onerous a chore as paying weekly installments on a household appliance that never seems to work when he wants it. Making love without pleasure is the first symptom of impotence and, if not arrested, eventually becomes a chronic condition.

A wonderfully simple, effective remedy is occasional coitus early in the morning after a refreshing night's sleep. Most men in reasonably good health periodically wake up with strong erections until they are in their seventies—proof that failure to produce a firm penis under other circumstances is psychic in origin or due to physical strain. Further, a man past forty who is worried by premature ejaculations can maintain his erection much longer when he is relaxed and delay his orgasm until his partner is reaching her own climax. The notion that sex is debilitating to a middle-aged man who has to get up and go to work is a complete fiction. It is such an exhilarating tonic that it can set him up for the entire day.

Morning intercourse may not be feasible as a regular procedure—which would defeat the purpose—but it hardly is a great imposition on a wife to accommodate her husband perhaps twice a month for a pleasant change of pace. And it ties in perfectly with the formula for erotic stimulation explained earlier. When a couple makes love only upon retiring for the night, a man seldom sees his wife exposed and ready to receive him. The sight of her body is wildly exciting to him, and, although male nudity usually does not arouse women, a wife gets reciprocal rewards. Her husband's heightened desire induces a stronger orgasm in her, and she hears reassuring expressions of tenderness that usually are omitted when he drops off to sleep after coitus.

Both partners are equal beneficiaries of sex play early in the morning, but it is a rare wife who does not recoil from an amorous caress upon awakening, as though it is an indecent proposal. A man stops making advances after years of rebuffs and, in brooding over them, may look for someone who is more receptive to him. When he finds her, the chief attraction of the affair may be the deviation from a set schedule of copulation. A mature woman who does go to bed with a man, whether her motive is matrimony, a good time, or a need for affection, always is more compliant than a wife. In the beginning, anyway. Every wife who loses her husband to another woman wonders what he sees in her. The answer simply may be that she indulges in the spontaneous flashes of desire a wife consistently suppresses when they do not suit her convenience.

It is not a facetious observation that the late talk shows and late, late movies on television have done more mischief to marital relations in America than adultery. This was suggested during the power failure that blacked out the northeastern part of the country on the night of November 9, 1965. Exactly nine months later hospitals in New York, Boston and other cities in the area reported an increase in births three to four times the normal rate. Sociologists gravely explained that in natural disasters people instinctively huddle together to reinforce interpersonal relationships and to allay their atavistic fear of darkness. Robert Hodges cut short his colleagues' elaborate theories with the obvious answer: "People went to bed because there was no television. Sex was the only amusement they had."

If television curbs so drastically the sexual activity of young couples, its effect on the middle aged hardly can be exaggerated. Men are guilty of antagonizing their wives on weekends by staring at sports events on the tube for stupefying hours on end, but women are the chief offenders in turning TV viewing into a nightly endurance contest that kills the amorous designs of husbands who generally get up an hour or two earlier in the morning. The idea of taking the initiative in love-making is alien to feminine pride, but every wife has a vital stake in maintaining sexual rapport with her husband. She can protect it by putting her arms around him occasionally and murmuring, "Let's not watch TV tonight."

"Women are demanding more sexual satisfaction, but they do not recognize that they must contribute to it," says Dr. Max Markowitz, director of the adult clinic at the Postgraduate Center for Psychotherapy in New York. "They always blame husbands for their disappointments and failures to have stronger orgasms. The reverse is true, more often than not. A woman must learn to provide her own peaks of emotional release and find the fulfillment of sex within herself.

"I see plenty of marital sex problems in the clinic and 95 percent of them can be traced to immaturity on one side of the bed. There are men who have not outgrown an adolescent need for constant approval and are uncertain of their virility in middle age, but just as many wives have reneged on the sexual responsibilities that are implicit in marriage. A common complaint of discontented wives is, 'He treats me like a sex object. All he cares about is his own selfish pleasure.' Then you hear husbands say, 'She lies there like a log. I'm tired of making love in a vacuum.'

"Who is at fault? It's unfair to indict women generally, but I'm convinced that far fewer marriages would wind up in divorce or reach our files if wives met their husbands halfway in an effort to resolve such conflicts. Merely submitting to a man is not enough. A wife must be an active participant in every phase of intercourse, from the preliminaries to the climax, to keep a sexual relationship viable."

Foreplay is the threshold to gratification many couples never cross or, at best, approach tentatively. Once they are joined in coitus their reactions are involuntary and vary slightly as they progress toward an orgasm. The quality of each sexual episode stems from the finesse in love-making that precedes intromission and is an increasingly important source

of enjoyment for experienced partners who appreciate subtlety.

The techniques a married couple employ in foreplay invariably are introduced by the husband, and it is a melancholy
fact that many men are inept lovers. Some authorities contend
that female frigidity is a man-made condition, pointing out
that virtually every woman who is unable to reach an orgasm
in coitus has no difficulty when she resorts to masturbation or
homosexual contacts. A few years ago Dr. Harold Leif, a psychiatrist at Tulane, interviewed interns in the University hospital and found that married as well as single men were
"abysmally ignorant" in rudimentary knowledge of sexual
responses despite their advanced study of anatomy and the
nervous system. Dr. Leif initiated a course in sex education in
the medical school, and some thirty institutions since have followed suit. The courses are partly subsidized by The Commonwealth Fund, an old medical foundation, to enable family
physicians to give competent advice to patients with sexual
problems.

It is a valuable program and long overdue, but sexual guid-
ance is not so much a matter of instruction in the mechanics of
mating as ridding people of guilt feelings that certain thoroughly natural impulses are perversions. Practices once mentioned only in textbooks on abnormal behavior are discussed
so openly now it is hard to believe that informed adults still
are inhibited in foreplay by fears of violating moral taboos.
Yet there are women of the postwar generation who have
never touched their husbands' genitals or appeared undressed
before them, and there are men who think it is depraved to
kiss their wives anywhere except the lips. Modesty and inno-
cence may be charming on the honeymoon, but refusal to
experiment with new methods of arousal after years of intimacy can be as damaging to a sexual relationship as the most
morbid aberration.

Sigmund Freud, who was described by Ernest Jones, his
biographer, as an "unusually chaste person—the word puri-

tanical would not be out of place," drew a clear distinction between perversion and wholesome sexuality: Anything a man and a woman consent to do in private is permissible as long as it is not made a regular substitute for orgasms reached in coitus. Freud's sex drive was so low that when he was forty-one he confided in a letter to an old friend, "Sexual excitation is of no more use to a person like me." He had the scientific objectivity to appreciate, however, that an active, vigorous libido thrives on varied and inventive stimulation. In commenting on "an indispensable condition of sexual enjoyment," such as viewing, fondling or kissing genital organs, Freud declared in a public lecture at the University of Vienna in 1917:

"It would be absurd to exclude people with single idiosyncrasies of this kind from the ranks of the normal and place them among perverts. Rather, it becomes more and more clear that what is essential to the perversions lies, not in the overstepping of the sexual aim, not in the replacement of the genitalia, not always even in the variations on the object, but solely in the *exclusiveness* with which these deviations are maintained, so that the sexual act which serves the reproductive process is rejected altogether. In so far as perverse performances are included in order to intensify or to lead up to the performance of the normal sex act, they no longer are actually perverse."

Freud's assertion that the basic difference between proper and corrupt sexual behavior is in degree, not in kind, was denounced as an endorsement of degeneracy. Critics were especially outraged by his tacit approval of mouth-genital contacts, a subject so hush-hush that Krafft-Ebing used the Latin terms, fellatio and cunnilingus, in guarded references to it in his volumes on sexual aberrations. Colleagues who had supported Freud's earlier controversial theories ostracized him for advocating in marriage an "unnatural appetite" supposedly catered to in brothels specializing in deviations.

Havelock Ellis, who did more to take the leer out of sex

than anyone except Freud, was a target for similar attacks when his landmark work, *Studies in the Psychology of Sex*, was published. Self-appointed censors here and abroad banned it as pornography for defending, among other things, the genital kiss and *soixante-neuf* (reciprocal oral stimulation) as acceptable practices. It was impossible, however, to suppress articles in professional journals and books written by physicians who gradually joined Freud and Ellis in giving the public new insights into sex. A recurring theme was summed up in 1930 by Dr. Robert L. Dickinson, a leading gynecologist: "A woman should be assured that there is nothing in the fullest sweep of passion that is not compatible with her highest ideals of spiritual love, and that all mutual intimacy of behavior is right between husband and wife."

Candor was the catalyst that brought a remarkable change in the most delicate area of our sexual mores. When Kinsey began collecting his data in 1938, a substantial number of men and women in the statistical sample were past thirty-five and had been brought up under a stricter moral code than subjects whose sexual experience began in the permissive climate ushered in by the jazz era of the 1920's. One of the great surprises in the Kinsey reports was the negligible difference between the two age groups in genital kissing during foreplay. About 60 percent of both the older and younger married people who had been to college engaged in it. There was a sharp drop to 20 percent among couples who had not gone beyond high school and to 11 percent for those whose education stopped after grade school.

"Because of the long-standing taboos in our culture on mouth-genital activity," Kinsey commented, "it is quite probable that there has been more cover-up on this point than on most others in the present study, and the above figures must, therefore, represent minimum incidences." Kinsey's estimates have been outdated by a marked slackening of inhibitions with the rise in the level of education, a strong influence in shaping more sophisticated sexual attitudes. This is clearly indicated by the sharp increase in the rate of divorce—formerly an upper-class luxury—among blue-collar workers with technical training.

Until a few years ago, virtually all divorce suits were instituted by wives on grounds of desertion or nonsupport. Today a common charge is mental cruelty, often the discreet term for conflicts over the wife's refusal to comply with her husband's insistance on oral stimulation during foreplay. Conversely, the middle-class divorce rate has remained stable for more than a decade.

Aversion to any form of heterosexual activity other than coitus generally is rooted in a strict religious background that condemns physical passion as lust. The birth-control controversy within the Catholic Church is only one facet of a grass-roots movement to liberalize its traditional restrictions on sexual practices. Father James Kavanaugh, a young priest with a Ph.D. in psychology, was relieved of his clerical duties in Michigan in 1966 for declaring that obsession with "purity can be proof of neurotic guilt or fear of physical love." The suppression of unorthodoxy has not resolved, however, the dilemma of priests who cannot find meaningful answers in medieval dogma for their parishioners' sexual problems.

A revealing insight into the private doubts racking one veteran priest comes from a young woman social worker for a Catholic family service agency. She recently was assigned to the case of a forty-two-year-old woman who had attempted to commit suicide.

"Do you know how a devout Catholic regards suicide?" she asked me.

"As a mortal sin?"

"Yes, and it's punishable by eternal damnation. That's what stunned everyone who knew Margaret. To hear them talk, she was the soul of piety who lived only for the church. She must have been temporarily deranged by some terrible feeling of guilt, and it did not take long to get a clue to it. She became frantic when I broached the subject of sex after asking her a few standard questions. Her face was contorted by a look of revulsion, and she clutched at herself as though she was contaminated by something unclean. When I tried to soothe her by saying that her trouble was not as bad as she thought it was, she cried, 'Father Brennan knows! Father Brennan knows my transgressions!' She obviously had confessed her offense to Father Brennan—that's not his real name—but I knew it was futile to ask him for information, because the confidences of the confessional are inviolate.

"Margaret remained in such an agitated state for a week that I was afraid she would go off the deep end again. I suggested that she enter a state mental hospital for her own safety, but her reaction was so violent that I knew she would never commit herself voluntarily. When I told my director that Margaret was a definite suicidal risk, he went to the bishop of the diocese and got a ruling that is so rare very few Catholics have ever heard of it.

"In certain emergencies a priest can divulge a confession with the consent of the penitent. I'm told it's a dispensation intended mainly for people who are dying and sinking too fast to give testimony that will clear innocent parties accused of their crimes. The bishop extended the ruling to overcome Margaret's mental block, but it was no immediate help to me. She flew into a panic and said her sins were too shameful for Father Brennan to repeat. I finally decided to give her the shock treatment. I told her she would try to kill herself again unless we found out what was weighing so heavily on her conscience. That did it. The fear of dying without absolution was stronger than her sense of guilt. She said she could not bear to tell a stranger what she had done, but she gave Father Brennan permission to disclose what he knew.

"The poor man was horribly embarrassed. It was the first time in his life he had ever discussed sex with a woman face-to-face. Despite the bishop's dispensation, I knew he felt that he was desecrating the confessional by betraying Margaret's secrets. Worst of all, he thought he was partly responsible for her crack-up, and talking about it was opening an old, painful wound.

"Margaret was about nine years old when Father Brennan was assigned to the parish after his ordination, and she became his special protégé as the first child in the congregation to show an interest in taking holy orders. He gave her private instruction in Church history, the lives of the saints and the Latin liturgy. Girls who talk of taking vows as nuns at that early age usually are pushed into it by their parents, but Margaret evidently had made the decision herself. She was a withdrawn child, so straitlaced that the other girls resented the holier-than-thou airs she put on. She had no friends and never had gone out with a boy until the night she graduated from parochial high school in 1944. The occasion was a party given by the church for the boys in the parish who were about to go into military service.

"It was Margaret's first date, and she didn't know what to expect when a boy named Joe, who lived on the same block, inveigled her into a parked car. He started to neck with her, and before she realized what he was up to his hands were all over her. Father Brennan was too mortified to repeat what Margaret had told him beyond saying that Joe 'invaded her privacy.' I asked him point-blank whether they had intercourse, and he shook his head. I gathered that Joe brought Margaret to an orgasm manually, but she was so naive she thought she had lost her virginity. At her next confession she told Father Brennan that she was defiled and could not take the veil.

" 'God forgive me for my intolerance,' Father Brennan said, 'but I gave her no solace. I honestly believed she lacked the strength of moral character required of a nun, and I did nothing to dissuade her. I condemned her with my silence.'

"The collapse of her sheltered little world started a chain of emotional crises for Margaret. She accused Joe of 'ruining' her and insisted they had to get married. She made such a scene on the street that the scared kid agreed to it to keep her quiet. Maybe he thought he would be arrested for attacking her or he hoped to get out of the draft. Whatever the reason, it was a disaster for both of them. The sudden wedding set off the usual gossip in the neighborhood. Her parents were convinced that she was pregnant. They were grim, ignorant people and treated her as though she had disgraced them.

"She did get pregnant three months after the wedding, the very first time she had intercourse with Joe. She had been so revolted by his pawing in the car that she wouldn't let him touch her, and he finally forced her to submit. That intensified her horror of sex, and, to make matters worse, her mother was one of those crabbed shrews who never let their husbands forget the few hours of pain they have in labor. Margaret had heard so many awful stories about childbirth that she was mortally afraid of it. Joe was drafted before she knew she was pregnant, and the rough time her parents gave her did not help the situation. After her baby, a girl, was born, she told Father Brennan that she had prayed for a miscarriage. That gave her another guilt complex. She had been unworthy of a nun's vows, and then, in her mind, she was unfit as a mother.

"Margaret blamed sex for her fall from grace, and it became such an obsession that when Joe returned from the Army she made him take a job on the night shift in the post office to avoid sleeping with him. 'I got so fed up with her carrying on about the sins of the flesh that I was glad to get out of the house,' Joe told me. 'Every time I tried to get close to her she yelled at me like I was a sex maniac and ran to church to pray for redemption. Some sex maniac. I haven't had a woman in twenty years, maybe more. I've lost count. I've been living with a nun instead of a wife.'

"You'd think abstinence would have killed Margaret's sex

drive, which never could have been very strong, but it flared up suddenly when a young man and his family moved into the house next door. Father Brennan is positive the man did nothing to encourage her, and I believe it. She always had been a plain Jane, and as far as the man was concerned she was a dowdy, middle-aged woman who was something of an eccentric. He had such an overwhelming physical attraction for her, though, that she began to watch his bedroom to sneak glimpses of him undressed.

"One night she heard the couple come home late. She knew the man let his dog out for a run in the backyard before retiring. Margaret took off her nightgown and went downstairs to seduce him. The psychiatrist who is treating Margaret now told me that unstable people gripped by a vivid fantasy sometimes work themselves into an autohypnotic state, and that evidently was what happened to her. She was snapped out of her trance by the dog's barking when it heard her open the back door.

"When Margaret realized she had gone out of the house stark naked, she ran to her room screaming hysterically for Father Brennan to hear her confession. Her daughter called him, and he was so shocked by the incident that the only penance he could think of was to tell her to read the temptations of St. Anthony. When he left, she slashed her wrists.

"Father Brennan looked as though he had aged twenty years when he finished the story. 'How did I fail Margaret?' he asked me. 'I know this never would have happened if not for that one experience when she was a girl. Was it wrong of me to rebuke her so harshly for a lapse that was not really her fault?'

"I told him I made no moral judgments. He held his head in his hands and said, 'I must—God help me.' "

In every religion there is a hard core of fanatics with a fifteenth-century mentality and a matching moral code they would impose on society. Their bitter rear-guard opposition to the enjoyment of sex as a natural function has been shattered by a twentieth-century weapon—the public survey. Although statistical studies of sexual behavior are criticized for fostering a "group think" morality, they serve one salutary purpose that possibly outweighs the objections. Disclosures that old taboos are widely ignored in marital intercourse have promoted the free expression of erotic drives, which certainly is healthier than practicing them as secret vices.

Something enormously significant has happened to middle-class mores when mouth-genital contacts, once considered a perversion, are accepted as a conventional technique in less than a generation. The French movie industry never has been reticent in exploiting sex at the box office, but the sponsors of the 1967 Cannes Film Festival refused to exhibit James Joyce's *Ulysses* until an allusion to the genital kiss was cut from Molly Bloom's famous soliloquy. The sequence was left intact in performances throughout the United States without protests from organizations that formerly had boycotted pictures showing a married couple in a double bed.

Exploring different methods of arousal adds to the zest of sex, of course, but experience teaches a man that novelty is overrated as an aphrodisiac. In middle age he is amused when he recalls heated schoolboy debates on the number of possible positions in copulation—a subject that permitted extravagant flights of imagination since none of the participants made any personal research in the field. The magic number ranged from sixty-four to "eighty-something," depending on interpretation of the *Kama Sutra*—a Sanskrit love manual that has been a hardy perennial in book stores since it was pirated by an enterprising English pornographer in the nineteenth century.

The *Kama Sutra* purportedly was written some fifteen hundred years ago by Vatsyayana, a Hindu poet, but it is suspected that Brahmins with exotic fixations later elaborated on the text. The primer describes in flowery detail a hodgepodge of gambits in intercourse, but the variations are as minute as the differences among the flakes of tobacco in a cigarette. The

Greeks, who were highly inventive in the erotic arts, were so impressed by the twelve positions reputedly employed professionally by Cyrene, an acrobatic courtesan, that Aristophanes commemorated her in a play.

Modern manuals list six positions, but three—sitting, standing and intromission from the rear—generally are discarded early in marriage or an affair after experiments with them as amusing diversions. They do not permit the deep penetration and the strong thrusting movements that intensify the gratification of both participants at the climax. In Western countries, most couples vary only occasionally from copulating in the two positions, with the male mounted on the female or lying beside her. Most women are strangely reluctant to employ regularly the position that is most exciting for them and their partners—on top of the male. This inhibition, which is peculiar to Judeo-Christian culture, began as an ascetic reaction to the hedonism of the Greeks and Romans, who preferred the female astride them. It was the universal procedure throughout the ancient civilized world, and except in the West it still is used more extensively than any other method.

A woman who has difficulty reaching an orgasm when she is supine usually achieves it more readily in the superior position. Her freedom of movement enables her to control the rhythm she desires on successive levels of tension and to keep her sensitive centers of arousal in constant contact with the penis. In mounting her lover she seems, psychologically, to take the initiative in soliciting his sexual favors, a conceit that never fails to increase his passion. Middle-aged wives who still are restrained by marriage manuals written a generation ago probably do not know that the shift from the standard position no longer is considered a reversal of roles that denotes latent homosexual tendencies in both partners. That was a popular theory in the early days of psychiatry, when labels were pinned on every "abnormal" impulse for instant identification on a Freudian chart.

Another archaic carry-over that is a common complication

in marriage is the erroneous notion that a couple must have simultaneous orgasms for complete satisfaction. The husband is charged with the responsibility of regulating his ejaculation to coincide precisely with his wife's climax, and if there is a slip-up in timing he is, by implication, a bungling lover. Unlike most fallacies about sex, the origin of this one is known. It was concocted by Dr. Theodore Van de Velde, a Dutch gynecologist who wrote *Ideal Marriage,* an enormously popular manual that was published in 1926 and promptly plagiarized with all its misinformation.

"In normal and perfect coitus," Van de Velde declared, "mutual orgasms must be almost simultaneous; the usual procedure is that the man's ejaculation begins and sets the woman's acme of sensation in train at once. The time it takes for the sensation received by the woman to reach her central nervous system and translate itself into supreme delight is less than a second. Such is the marvelous rate of nervous transmission."

Such is the marvelous ignorance of sex that some husbands make love anxiously gauging their wives' response, as though they are sprinters who will be disqualified from the race if they do not hit the finish line in a dead heat. The analogy is no more absurd than Van de Velde's flat assertion that the most complex of all human reactions must be synchronized within one second for thorough rapport in bed.

Simultaneous orgasms are wonderfully exhilarating, of course, but such a chancy concurrence of intangibles is involved that the odds are heavily stacked against a well-mated couple having them consistently. Sexual desire in men and women fluctuates so erratically that it is purely a happy accident when they reach a climax together. Fatigue or mental pressures can cause a man to ejaculate as soon as he enters the vagina. The identical factors may make it impossible for a woman to have an orgasm on any given night despite her partner's skillful foreplay and prolonged self-control. The libido is most active in some women just before the menstrual period; in others the peak is just after it. The pattern of a woman's orgastic cycle may be disrupted after she goes through the menopause and may require a good deal of re-adjustment.

Since a man usually reaches a climax faster than a woman, he often feels guilty of spoiling her pleasure by failing to maintain a strong erection until she arrives on the final plateau of arousal. A middle-aged husband who has been satisfying his wife for many years should not be concerned by an occasional misfire. She is not. Feeling his virility pour into her is a profound—perhaps the supreme—tribute to her femininity. Her own climax may be most intense when it is a chain reaction set off by his orgasm.

Couples who follow the book too literally and are disturbed by the inability to coordinate their orgasms invariably exaggerate wildly the difference in timing. Sexual tension distorts all sensory perceptions, especially the concept of time. A minute seems an eternity on the brink of an orgasm. An experienced woman's climax rarely is more than thirty seconds later than a man's—the average is less than fifteen seconds—yet people seeking professional advice for correcting the difficulty talk as though there is an interminable delay that exhausts them physically and emotionally.

When faulty timing becomes a problem to a middle-aged couple who previously were not bothered by it, the calendar rather than the clock is the culprit. The declining rate of marital intercourse operates at cross-purposes on each partner. It tends to speed up a man's reaction and slow down a woman's as the intervals between coitus lengthen and the delicate network of nervous impulses that triggers an orgasm loses resilience through disuse. Regular sexual activity keeps the balance wheel of the timing mechanism in prime working order.

Prolonged foreplay is an increasingly valuable ally to a man after forty in compensating for a woman's slower arousal and advancing her toward an orgasm before coitus begins. Too many husbands, bored by a self-imposed routine, go through the preliminaries in an apathetic manner that does not inspire their wives to imaginative sex play. It is an aptitude easy to cultivate, for men and women are so alike anatomically that any erotic stimulus that delights one partner is almost certain to titillate the other.

For example, men universally fondle and kiss the female's breasts in foreplay. The male's nipples are as sensitive to touch, yet most women never make that discovery. Their spontaneity and curiosity are stifled by tedious love-making; they lose interest in sex when the romantic expectations they bring to the marriage bed languish on the vine. "Marriage must continually vanquish a monster that devours everyone, the monster of habit," Balzac said. It never is too late to experiment with new techniques. They are all the more exciting when discovered in middle age.

One fine technicality will increase a couple's mutual enjoyment of intercourse immeasureably. A man comes to a full erection so quickly and involuntarily he does not know that it is essential to stimulate continuously a woman's genital area throughout foreplay and coitus. The moment he stops, her level of arousal drops precipitously, even in the middle of an orgasm. Constant manual or oral contact must be maintained during foreplay, and after insertion the male's thrusting movements must be kept up without interruption.

Comes the critical point. If he reaches a climax first, it is imperative for him to continue thrusting to help her progress, steadily and smoothly, toward her orgasm. He should not lie inertly, in deep penetration, after he ejaculates. The period of inactivity, brief as it may be, can set her back to the first phase. If his loss of tumescence does not permit strong thrusts, he should resume manual stimulation. It is a mistake, albeit a natural one, to search for the small, elusive clitoris. Dr.

Masters' research at Washington University revealed that as a woman's sexual tension approaches the peak her clitoris shifts from its normal position and retracts under a hood that is inaccessible to the fingers. She can be brought to a gratifying orgasm by manipulating the labia at the entrance to the vagina.

What other practical advice can be given for an active, pleasurable sex life after forty? None that any man who has been through the mill and possesses common sense does not already know—even though he may not follow it. Only fools and charlatans recommend clever ploys and tricks that are guaranteed to make a woman a slave to love. The libido of every individual is as distinctive as each set of fingerprints. Beyond a few basic physical reactions, the chemistry of sexual attraction is unpredictable.

Spontaneity is the key to the flashes of desire that recharge a middle-aged man's potency, but it presupposes a readiness for sex that is lacking when he has depleted his stockpile of physical resources. If sex is important to him, as it should be to affirm his masculinity, he must ration his reserve of energy after the demands of work have been met. He cannot scatter it all over the golf course on weekends or leave it on the rocks of his fourth Scotch after dinner and expect to perform lustily in bed that night.

Several years ago I wrote an as-told-to article with William Benton for *The Saturday Evening Post* criticizing the caliber of business education in American colleges. Benton, publisher of the *Encyclopaedia Britannica,* charged that he had been a cultural illiterate upon graduation from Yale in 1921 after taking a curriculum that had the intellectual substance of a comic strip. The boy wonder of advertising during the Depression, Benton made enough money to retire at the age of thirty-six, just seven years after opening an agency with Chester Bowles, and then devoted himself to public affairs. Among other things, he was vice-president of the University of Chicago, Assistant Secretary of State, U.S. Senator from Connecticut, founder of the Committee for Economic Development and a delegate to numerous UNESCO and inter-American conferences.

In the course of research for the article I asked Stanley Teele, dean of the Harvard Business School, what is the most important attribute of a successful corporation executive. "If I knew the answer, I'd be running General Motors as a sideline on weekends," Teele replied. "Top management calls for such a combination of diverse talents that it's impossible to say one qualification takes precedence over all others."

Benton dismissed Teele's comment with an impatient wave of the hand when I repeated it to him. "I know the answer," he snapped. "It has nothing to do with intelligence or ability. It's strictly a matter of luck in having been born with a cast-iron constitution. Every successful political figure, industrialist and creative person I've ever known has been a horse for work. His motivation to acquire money or power or prestige is stronger than the average fellow's, but his ambition is not worth a damn if he cannot carry a work load that competitors are unable, or unwilling, to tackle.

"Human dynamos who never seem to run out of steam don't press their luck. They know there is a limit to their endurance as they get older and pace themselves accordingly. When they unwind, they pick their spots to get the most fun out of it, just as they lay out work schedules for maximum efficiency. They allow time to recuperate their energy so that they are fresh for whatever is next on the agenda. It's simply a matter of putting first things first, whether it's business or pleasure."

Sex is man's greatest pleasure, but he does not give it proper priority in his design for living. He stumbles into traps that erode his enjoyment of it, then perversely digs himself deeper into the holes. For example, a man who lives in the suburbs may be more potent in an extramarital affair simply because the rendezvous is in town and he copulates before going through the drudgery of commuting. A majority of the middle-class men in America commute to work—a tortuous grind that takes two or three hours a day out of their lives and an incalculable toll of their vitality and good nature.

The considerations that prompted a young father to move to the suburbs—uncrowded schools for the children, better recreational facilities for the entire family—no longer are pertinent when he is past fifty. His children are grown; he and his wife rattle around a bigger house than they need—or should carry; his participation in outdoor activities necessarily is curtailed; he is taxed heavily for services and conveniences he does not use. Men who move back to town closer to their work invariably are happier for it, even though their wives at first are not.

As a rule, young wives are opposed to the isolation of the suburbs that confines them to domestic chores. Twenty years later they resist leaving friends and the comforts of a leisurely routine to contend with the turmoil of city life. It is, admittedly, a more difficult readjustment for a woman, but if she recognizes the benefits to her husband, the intellectual stimulation of the city can compensate for the personal sacrifices she makes.

Even more understanding is required of a wife to relieve the worst drain on a man's sexual capability—financial pressures. All the arguments exhorting wives to ease the demands on aging husbands boil down to one question: "Madam, would you rather sleep with a mink coat or a warm, responsive husband?"

# 11

# "Oh, To Be Seventy Again!"

✽✽✽

SOCIETY'S ANTAGONISM TO SEX IN OLD AGE CAN BE SUMMED up in seven words: Virility at twenty-five is lechery at sixty-five. Sexuality in elderly people expresses their increasing need for the emotional support of love and intimacy to offset their feelings of rejection. Although they may be capable of intercourse only once a month, it gives the morale of aging couples a vital lift, but most widowers who would like to remarry abandon the thought rather than alienate their families. The warped attitude of middle-aged children that sex is indecent at their age condemns them—and widows with whom they could find contentment—to loneliness that is more devastating than disease.

The tangible benefits the elderly derive from sexual activity are not romantic fantasies. U.S. Public Health Service statistics show decisively that married people live longer than single, divorced or widowed persons. After sixty-five, a man whose wife is living has almost twice as good a chance as a bachelor of surviving from one year to the next. The differential for women is not quite as sharp, because their life spans are longer in all categories, but the probability that a married woman past sixty-five will celebrate her next birthday is about one-third better than a widow's. Further, the survival odds favoring the married group have lengthened steadily during the last half-century.

Sex after sixty is largely contingent upon the availability of a partner who is, with rare exceptions, the spouse. Related factors promote the longevity of married couples, of course. Companionship, a sense of responsibility for someone, sympathetic attention in sickness and regular eating habits all contribute to the well-being of elderly couples. Their physical gratification from intercourse may be minimal, but psychologically it is their strongest link with the life force. The assurance that they still can function on that basic biological level alleviates, in some measure, their feeling of helplessness as other powers decline.

Intellectually, we concede that it is infinitely better for an aging man or woman to share a bed with a sexually active partner than to slip into senescence in it alone. We admire an Oliver Wendell Holmes II for refusing to let time corrode his indomitable *joie de vivre*. A year or so before his death at the age of ninety-four, Holmes was taking a stroll in Washington with Louis Brandeis, his old friend and colleague in the Supreme Court, when they passed a pretty girl. Justice Holmes turned and looked appreciatively at her fetching contour.

"Oh, to be seventy again!" the old gentleman said wistfully.

Yet mature sons and daughters, who smile indulgently at the story, recoil as though a widowed father is a dirty old man if he has an affair or sees a woman a few years younger than him. Copulation is permissible for other parents, but not their own. Their hostility forces many aging people to renounce the affection that could enrich their final years. They are prisoners of the lifelong shame of sex inculcated in them by the mores of society.

*Geriatrics,* a medical journal specializing in problems of aging, has commented editorially: "Elderly men and women often refrain from continuing their sexual relations or from seeking remarriage after the loss of a spouse because even they themselves have come to regard sex as a little ridiculous, so much have our social attitudes equated sex with youth." When potent men in their sixties and seventies suddenly stop inter-

course with their wives, the usual rationalization is that dignified companionship is the only proper marital bond at their
age. The basic reason is that they are ashamed of their sexual
urges.

"Despite the large number of voluntary dropouts, regular
intercourse is the rule rather than the exception for couples
after sixty-five, and it continues as long as they are in reasonably good health," says Theodore Isenstadt. He was the director of a study on aging conducted by the Family Services
Association of America on a grant from the Ford Foundation. "Interest in sex is much higher among the elderly than
younger people suspect. It is concealed to avert clashes with
relatives who think it is a sign of depravity or senility. Old
folks also are inhibited by a feeling of guilt, a carry-over of the
embarrassment they felt as adolescents when they associated
their own parents with sex.

"These restraints largely disappear in a segregated environment, such as a home for the aged, where there is no inter-
ference in social contacts with people of their own generation.
They talk about sex constantly, and if they are widowed they
seek outlets for their physical desire. Every year there are approximately thirty-five thousand marriages in which both
parties are past sixty-five. Their families assume they want
companionship and someone to look after them. This may
come as a shock, but old folks marry primarily for sex. I'll let
you in on another surprise. They generally have a more con-
genial relationship than young couples.

"It is a standing joke among gerontologists that late marriages work out well, because there is no mother-in-law trouble. In the same humorous vein you also can say there are no
conflicts over philandering and children, two common causes
of friction between young husbands and wives. The down-to-
earth reason for the success of the marriages is pretty somber
—the imminence of death. Elderly people know that they
have only a few years left together, and they try to make the

most of them. They can't afford to waste time on petty squabbles."

A sudden flare-up of the libido in old age is a common phenomenon called the "clinging-to-life syndrome," which can occur after many years of total continence. Elderly women who have had no sexual experiences since they were widowed in middle age often show the strongest manifestations. The revival of an urgent desire for intercourse is a reaction to aging and the inevitability of death. Performing the sex act is their identification with the continuity of life.

A similar reaction is the ravenous appetites for food of relatives and friends immediately after someone close to them has died. Despite their genuine grief the survivors subconsciously say, "Thank God it wasn't me." They crave food to strengthen their hold on life. Later, they are guilt-stricken by their apparent insensitivity, but it is an entirely natural impulse. All cultures recognize it with the wakes and feasts of the funeral ceremony.

Physical contact is a component of life as essential as food and shelter. The appalling mortality of infants in orphanages years ago was not due to malnutrition or deficient hygienic measures. Children born to poverty-stricken slum families were raised under worse conditions, but the great majority of them thrived on love and attention. The orphans died of emotional deprivation—they literally wasted away for lack of affectionate fondling. It is standard procedure now in progressive hospitals and institutions for nursery attendants to pick up and fondle newborn babies several times a day to give them the security of human touch. But at the opposite pole of the life cycle, more discarded and displaced old people are succumbing to emotional deprivation than ever before.

The best medicine for them was prescribed recently by Dr. Sidney Levin, a Boston psychoanalyst: "It has been observed by many physicians that when they visit elderly patients the introduction of only minor bodily contact, such as holding the patient's hand, may be experienced by the patient with great pleasure. Such an experience can represent a major form of sexual satisfaction for a person whose bodily contacts with others have been seriously restricted."

It may seem absurd to speak of a pat on the hand as sexual satisfaction, because we make the mistake of thinking of sex only in terms of genital gratification instead of emotional fulfillment. The personality traits of the elderly that irritate younger people are defensive patterns to cushion daily blows to their self-esteem. In the grave-side scene in *Death of a Salesman,* Willy Loman's widow cried that the beaten and the discouraged "demand consideration," but no one listened—then, or now.

Old people repeat stories interminably to impress an audience—any audience—with their former importance and achievements. They forget a message ten minutes after it is given to them, but they remember with perfect clarity the details of an incident that happened forty years ago. Why? They cling to memories of the past, when they were vigorous and productive, to blot out the bleak present and the dismal future. They constantly grouse about food, their infirmities and the disappointments of life to gain sympathy and attention. Their incessant verbalization—"I'm going down to the drugstore later on to get that salve that's so good for my arthritis, and then I'm going to take a nice walk in the park, because it's so pretty this time of year, and then I'm going to watch that Clark Gable movie on TV your father and I saw on our trip to St. Louis when we visited my sister"—are efforts to communicate with people who have relegated them to a vacuum.

"One must wait until the evening to see how splendid the day has been," Sophocles wrote in a more gracious time, when the elderly were respected for their wisdom and experience. Judson Landis, a sociologist, asked a cross section of 450 men and women past sixty-five what they regarded as the happiest stage of their lives. Half the group selected the period between twenty-five and forty-five; 20 percent chose the years between fifteen and twenty-five; 18 percent preferred childhood; 7 percent had no definite opinion. The remaining 5 percent chose the decade after forty-five. Not a single vote was cast for old age.

The most depressing aspect of growing old is not the loss of physical strength, earning power or friends. It is the realization that society suffers the elderly as though they are parasites with no useful function. Everyone getting on in years feels a poignant sense of futility, but there is no question that men are affected by it more severely. Women themselves admit that they can cope better with the emptiness of old age. It may be a more significant factor in the female's longevity than her stronger resistance to infirmities and diseases.

"A woman is a high priestess of little things," Carl Jung said. She can keep herself occupied in old age with news of children and relatives, fussing with household chores, shopping and small talk with acquaintances, activities that are not much different from her usual lifelong routine. She is permitted more outlets for her libido—call it maternal love, if you will—in kissing and fondling children. A man who lavishes too much affection on his own grandchild is uncomfortably aware that people look askance at him. A woman's interests largely revolve around interpersonal relationships, and she is never completely isolated from them. A man's attention is focused on achievement rather than people, and when his working career is ended, by debility or compulsory retirement, he is cut off from the dominant motivation of his adult life.

Surely the most senseless policy adopted in public and private sectors of employment in this century is compulsory retirement at sixty-five. Arguing that chronological age is no index to a man's mental or creative capability is belaboring a point as obvious as it is familiar. Men past seventy-five have been prominent in the center of the postwar political arena— Churchill, De Gaulle and Adenauer. Elderly committee chairman in Congress control legislation, and even older judges interpret it, yet an able-bodied man at the peak of his expertise rarely can get anything better than a subordinate job on the open labor market if he is past sixty.

Old age can be defined as that period of life which retreats farther into the future the closer you approach it. Sixty-five is an arbitrary milestone for the onset of senescence that most people refuse to acknowledge when they arrive there. Several years ago Cornell University made a study of 3515 workers in 265 industries who were within two years of retirement. The majority—68 percent—thought of themselves as middle-aged up to seventy-five.

Although an employee has known the exact date of his compulsory retirement since he was hired, it always comes as a profound shock to a man who has been contending with challenges all his life. On a Friday night he is pulling his weight as a productive member of the community. On Monday morning he is on the scrap heap. Two months later he discovers that leisure on a pension, described so alluringly in brochures put out by insurance companies, was a rotten carrot on a stick. The only men who welcome retirement quit competing for success early in their careers and take refuge in anonymity with a large corporation or a safe Civil Service job.

It is a monstrous hoax to tell a man that lazing in the sun or playing games or killing time with vacuous hobbies will be a satisfactory substitute for the purposeful objectives that stretched his intelligence and initiative. His mind demands meatier nourishment than the pap of recreation. Like a powerful car kept in low gear, he strains with unused energy that causes more wear and tear than running at normal cruising speed. Idleness does not even help his sex drive. After the novelty of leisure has passed, boredom and lack of mental stimulation cut his frequency of intercourse below the rate prior to his retirement.

Men who have pensions or other assured sources of income

that enable them to maintain a decent standard of living without working are the elderly elite. The majority exists on the ragged edge of indigence, dependent on Social Security benefits or handouts from their children. Primitive people who clubbed aged parents to death or turned them out to freeze when food was scarce were more humane than modern society. Death came quickly and was dignified by traditional ceremonies that honored their sacrifice as essential to the survival of the tribe. Today, the elderly are stripped of their self-respect if they do not have money to buy, and hold, the consideration of their families. They have no status. Their experience is ignored, and their cultural contributions are derided.

The plight of the elderly is another verse in the dirge of doom constantly drummed into us. We are told that the world is hellbent for disaster unless solutions are found for poverty, urban blight, racial conflicts, the population explosion and other social problems too tedious to enumerate. It is impossible for the individual to get wrought-up over every dire prediction. He must practice the selective apathy of the man who explained in the wry joke how decisions were made in his home: "I handle the big problems, like whether we should recognize Red China, and my wife handles the little ones, like whether we should have a baby."

One enormous difference makes the problems of aging more pertinent than all other thorny issues. The consequences of failure are not calamities of the vague future that will afflict strangers in a remote section of the globe. Everyone whose parents are frustrated and embittered can see the predicament in store for him if he has the dubious luck to reach old age without emotional resources to cope with it.

There are no easy solutions for the  proliferation of the elderly brought about by medical advances. Between 1900 and 1950, the census of the United States doubled, but the number of people past sixty-five more than quadrupled. In 1968 there were nineteen million. By 1975 they will comprise nearly 10 percent of the population, putting a heavy burden on the economy for ever-increasing Social Security benefits if they are not given opportunities to support themselves, at least partially.

The complications begin with housing. Three-generation households are disappearing rapidly, and the trend to urban living in small, expensive apartments is certain to compound the dislocation of the elderly. Nostalgic stories are told of the strong family ties that were forged when it was customary for grandparents to move in with married children, but it never was an ideal setup. There were inevitable conflicts among the adults, and the constant presence of ailing, querulous old folks had an oppressive effect on young children. Segregating the aged in institutions or special communities does not always work out satisfactorily even in the best facilities. Some residents are stimulated by group activities, but as many are depressed by the atmosphere. Under the most favorable circumstances there is an undercurrent of resentment for having been dumped into a repository for the useless.

The best arrangement is for elderly people to live alone in small apartments as long as they can fend for themselves, physically and financially. The health of the aged is surprisingly good, generally, until the onset of a terminal illness, but discrimination bars them from the economic independence that sustains their pride—a more fragile structure than the body. The prejudice against older workers is short-sighted on every count, starting with the obvious fact that business cannot afford to let their experience and skills go by the boards.

Every study of comparative job performance made by the Bureau of Labor Statistics has shown that men and women past sixty-five have a higher output of office work than people below thirty. The slighter slowness of the elderly is more than compensated by their consistency and superior caliber of work. They are more conscientious, because they are appreciative of the jobs they need urgently. Another recent disclosure made by the National Institute of Mental Health was, inferentially, an awful slap at the current quality of education. Men chosen at random, whose average age was seventy-two, had better command of the language than a control group of recent high-school graduates—an ability in very short supply in federal, state and local agencies that deal directly with the public.

Government bureaus on all levels eventually will have to absorb the surplus of elderly workers in part-time desk jobs, but another prejudice—the denial of their need for sex—will be more difficult to break down. The cruelest thing we do to old people is to treat them as though they are vegetables without instincts or feelings. The sex drive does not stop abruptly at a definite cutoff point after fifty years of activity. Grandfathers do not wear blinders that make them oblivious to miniskirts, risqué movies, suggestive pictures in magazines and other erotic influences that arouse younger men. Grandmothers still get a vicarious thrill watching TV reruns of movies with love scenes played by stars who once had sex appeal for them. Septuagenarians who try to attract the opposite sex may look pathetically grotesque to relatives, but they do not wither away in slippers and bathrobes. Their efforts to look well-groomed, to move sprightly and to make amusing small talk symbolize their will to live.

Much has been learned about sexuality in old age since Kinsey dismissed it by devoting only three of the seventeen hundred pages in his two books to the subject. By every reliable criterion, sex is as necessary for happiness and security in later years as in any other stage of life, yet it is a target for ridicule or hostility. Physicians are not exempt from the first charge. Dr. A. D. Claman, chairman of a symposium on sexual difficulties after fifty conducted by the Canadian Medical Association in 1966, declared:

"It is apparent that there are too many misconceptions about the role of sex in the lives of older people. Even doctors rarely ask their older patients about sex and they are, to some extent, embarrassed to initiate a discussion with people of the grandparent status. Most coffee-table talks among physicians on this subject are never very serious and consist of exchanging amusing stories about sex in older patients, as if such behavior were bizarre. Our aversion to serious discussions about sex in older people may be based on the fact that we identify old people with our own parents and are therefore made uncomfortable when we think of our parents in this connection."

An important new finding confirmed in numerous studies is that a sexually active man in reasonably good health does not suffer a decided drop in potency until he is well into the seventies—a decade beyond the period formerly believed to mark the onset of serious difficulty in achieving erections. Fully 70 percent of married men past sixty-five have intercourse regularly on an average of twice a month. Once a week is not unusual at seventy. Even in advanced ages there is no sudden loss of potency, barring illness. An eighty-year-old man's tapering off does not exceed the rate of his declining frequency when he was forty.

This benign slowdown grinds to an abrupt halt in men and women who are widowed after sixty. Sexual activity stops, completely and permanently, in the overwhelming majority of cases despite a resurgence of the libido after several months of mourning the death of a spouse. No matter how deeply a couple loved each other, the survivor frequently feels the insistent tug of sexual desire.

Aging widowed people usually pretend they are indifferent to sex, because they are acutely self-conscious of their loss of physical attractiveness. The fear of rebuffs inhibits them from seeking new partners, but they get over their sensitivity if they have social contacts with contemporaries in group activities or through introductions by friends. Rapport often is established quickly, but it rarely leads to an affair. Time tempers nonconformity; the elderly have too much respect for the marriage covenant to flout convention as they might have done twenty years earlier. A stronger deterrent stops them from a proper union—the stigma attached to sex in the later years.

The only available outlet for their sexual tensions is masturbation, a release that is as unsatisfactory as it is disturbing psychologically. Considerable evidence indicates that there is more masturbation by men and women after sixty than at any period except adolescence. It invariably is accompanied by feelings of guilt and frustration from having to resort to a practice they consider demeaning.

The largest sample of sexual habits and attitudes among the elderly ever accumulated was obtained by *Sexology* magazine from a questionnaire sent in 1959 to some six thousand men past sixty-five who were listed in *Who's Who in America*. The response was remarkable in view of the personal nature of the survey and the caliber of the subjects. Ordinarily, a response of 5 percent to a "blind" poll is considered good, but 832 men (14 percent) answered *Sexology*'s questions—a reflection of their anxieties. Among the married men who were potent up to the age of ninety-two, 70 percent reported that they had satisfactory intercourse regularly, yet despite their superior intelligence they confessed feelings of shame about their sexual desires. The editors conjectured that only 25 percent admitted they masturbated because of a deeper sense of guilt.

Antipathy to sex in old age has been made more obdurate by the offenses elderly men have committed against children. No attempt will be made here to gloss over such horrible crimes, infrequent as they are. One rape-killing a decade is one too many; it is outrageous that parents must warn children not to talk to strangers on the street. Society has every right to demand the confinement of men who are guilty of molesting youngsters, but it also should realize that the danger will not be eliminated until it corrects the conditions that provoke sexual perversions in old age.

"A great and unnecessary hardship has been visited upon

many elderly men and women by the traditional demand that all human beings, as they grow old, shall also grow asexual," Dr. Norman Cameron, of the Yale Psychiatric Institute, wrote in *Mental Disorders in Later Life*. "This may be true of other drives; but in the sexual field it seems also to be derived from one ancient prejudice identifying sex with sin and another denying the right of sinning to elderly men and women. These prejudices do not square with the well-known fact that some persons suffer little reduction in sexual ability up to an advanced age, and with at least casual evidence at hand to indicate that most persons retain some personal sex interest almost to the end of their lives."

The reason formerly given for deviant behavior in old age was that it resulted from brain degeneration that destroyed a senile man's sense of moral values. The problem would be much easier to control if this was the complete explanation. Cerebral damage can be detected when erratic conduct is a clue to potential trouble, but few elderly men who commit sex crimes show such pathological symptoms, nor are they senile.

An offense generally is the climax of a series of incidents that intensify an old man's feeling of alienation from his environment. When he is denied opportunities for normal heterosexual relations, he may look for an easy source of gratification. Since a mature woman is unavailable to him and will resist a forcible advance, he fixes his erotic attention upon a defenseless child. A criminal attack often begins with no malicious intent. The man fondles a little girl or boy to relieve his loneliness, then flies into a rage when he construes the child's terror as a rejection of his affection.

Widows who are left substantial estates frequently conform to a classic pattern in venting their resentment against families that oppose their remarriage, for valid or selfish reasons. An elderly woman who gets involved with a disreputable young character and then is fleeced by him in a brazen swindle that would not fool a child is thought to be senile, but she usually knows exactly what she is doing. She deliberately squanders the money that children and relatives expect to inherit to punish them for trying to stop her from going to bed with a more suitable partner.

A more serious complication, because it affects virtually every man, arises from the fallacies about the loss of sexual competence in later life, due to the impairment of certain organs. The most prevalent and persistent misconception concerns the prostate, a gland the size of a walnut located between the bladder and the urethra, the canal that carries urine and sperm. The principal function of the prostate is to ejaculate a milky fluid during an orgasm that helps to transport and nourish the sperm, but it is not a crucial part of the male's sexual apparatus. In most cases surgery does not interfere in any way with his ability to have a thoroughly satisfactory erection and orgasm, but a prostate operation has such dread connotations that most men are convinced it invariably leads to total impotence.

"In the whole field of male medicine no single ailment is the subject of more confusion, misinformation and out-and-out quackery than what is generally referred to, with somewhat ominous vagueness, as 'prostate trouble,' " Dr. Joseph Kaufman, a urologist at the University of California Medical School, writes in *Man and Sex*. "This is dangerous but not surprising because of all the physical disorders that are specifically male, those that involve the prostrate are the most common."

Once a man passes forty it is an even bet that sooner or later he will require some sort of prostate treatment, not necessarily surgery. If he must have an operation, he has a 70 percent chance of retaining—or regaining—his maximum potency. These are infinitely better odds than neglecting a serious condition. It always results in impotence.

The basic source of trouble is enlargement of the prostate, a part of the aging process caused by an imbalance of hormones. Other glands undergo similar changes without producing ill effects, but the growth of the prostate blocks the flow of urine from the bladder and may lead to a severe infection of the kidneys. The first symptoms usually are the need to urinate frequently, especially during the night, and a progressive slowing and weakening of the urinary stream. Hormone injections and prostate massages sometimes help to relieve discomfort and forestall an operation, but such measures do not cure the condition. A portion of the growth may have to be removed by surgery, but enough of the gland usually is left to permit intercourse without difficulty.

The only postoperative change may be a retrograde ejaculation, or a "dry run." All the sensations of an orgasm are felt, but the sperm flows into the bladder instead of the urethra, due to the removal of a small valve to prevent the spread of infection. Although the man is sterile, it hardly is a matter of critical concern at his age. Sterility is entirely unrelated to impotence.

Two other prostatic ailments require attention. One (prostatostasis) is caused by insufficient intercourse or improper techniques during it. The secretions from the prostate contain a sediment that blocks the ducts of the urethra if it is not flushed out regularly by strong ejaculations. Until the wife's menopause, some couples still resort to coitus interruptus, an old, dangerous form of birth control in which the husband withdraws before his orgasm. Prolonged sex play that does not culminate in intercourse also causes the condition. It can be relieved by hormones and massages, but the best therapy is frequent intercourse.

False alarms of impotence sometimes are set off by an inflammation of the gland (prostatitis) caused by the spread of an infection from another part of the body. The symptoms are painful ejaculations and acute fatigue after coitus. They can be cleared up, under a physician's care, of course, by rest, a bland diet, local heat and antibiotics.

It should be emphasized that the 30 percent who are rendered impotent by a prostatectomy are mostly men well past seventy, who would in any case be on the brink of sexual incompetence. The only operation that always results in impotence is for cancer of the prostate. Since the disease in that area is lethal, the alternative is easier to accept. If performed early enough a man's life expectancy is almost identical with that of men of the same age in the general population, but less than 10 percent of the cases are caught in time for effective surgery.

The American Cancer Society for years has been urging men past forty to have regular checkups for prostatic cancer, just as periodic Pap tests are recommended for women to detect cancer of the cervix. According to the A.C.S. statistics, about three times as many women as men voluntarily request such examinations. A survey made in 1966 of the public's attitude toward the A.C.S. educational campaign revealed that men thought it was "unmasculine" to be worried about the disease—a show of bravado that deluded no one. It betrayed their dread of impotence.

The best prognosis of a man's chances of regaining his maximum potency after a noncancerous prostatectomy comes from the patient himself. If he is eager to prove that he can still gratify a woman, the odds are heavily in his favor. As always, the psychological factor transcends the physical, regardless of a man's age.

"A potent aging male's responsive ability, dormant for physical or social reasons, can be restimulated if he wishes to return to active sexual practices and he has a partner interested in sexual performance," Dr. Masters asserted in *Human Sexual Response*. "If he is in adequate health, little is needed to support adequacy of sexual performance in a seventy- or even an eighty-year-old male other than some physiologic outlet or psychologic reason for reactivated sexual interest. Even if coital activity has been avoided for long periods of time, men in these age groups can be returned to effective sexual function if adequate stimulation is instituted and interested partners are available."

A word of caution: Miracles cannot be expected. Investigators occasionally come across hardy prodigies who are copulating regularly after ninety, but the vast majority of men lose the ability to produce an erection firm enough for intercourse in their late seventies or early eighties. The folklore of sex is replete with legends—none documented—of people who were active sexually at fantastic ages. Thomas (Old) Parr, an Englishman, reputedly remarried at 120, faithfully serviced his wife for twelve more years, and died at the age of 152. He was buried with great pomp in Westminster Abbey in 1635, not the first—or the last—in that pantheon with a tenuous claim to fame.

Christian Drakenberg, a great Dane, was said to have died at 146 in 1772 after a rather full life that included naval combat in four wars, fifteen years of slavery under Barbary pirates, a marriage at 111 and some strenuous woman-chasing following the death of his wife. Dr. Pierre Defournel insisted he was 102 when he married a woman seventy-six years younger and had several children by her. Active sperm capable of impregnating a woman reportedly was found in the semen of a 103-year-old Russian some sixty years ago. A Hungarian couple, John and Sara Roven, were celebrated for 147 years of marriage; he died at 172, she at 164. A tombstone in Carmarthen, England, would have tourists believe that Ann David was 181 when she expired in 1831.

In modern times Zaro Aga, a Turk, supposedly had outlived thirteen wives and most of his twenty-five children when he died in 1934 at 156. Sociologists who have studied the Lepchas, a primitive tribe of northern India as famous in the profession as the Jukes family, report astonishing daily rates of coitus by the oldest men, but only estimates can be made of their ages. Official birth records were not registered until the nineteenth century and are still unreliable in many countries.

There is a universal tendency to exaggerate age when some-one passes ninety. Although a few people undoubtedly have reached extreme ages, there is no definite evidence that any-one ever has lived more than 120 years.

Despite the medical advances of the last three thousand years, the Biblical pronouncement that three score and ten years is man's allotted term on earth remains a remarkably accurate forecast. Gerontologists have stopped searching for the panaceas to prolong life and vigor that were popular a half-century ago. Their principal objective now is to make the final years more comfortable and meaningful.

Since 1900, approximately twenty years have been added to life expectancy; in 1968 it was sixty-seven for men and seventy-four for women. But the chances of a sixty-five-year-old person living to seventy and beyond are no better today than they were in 1600. The increase in life expectancy is largely the result of the conquests of infectious diseases in infancy and childhood. If a cure for all forms of cancer was found tomorrow, only 1.8 years would be added to the anticipated life span of an adolescent. If all diseases were wiped out, no one could expect to live beyond eighty.

Old age is incurable, but a sexual relationship founded on reciprocal love can make it easier to bear. And when that prop finally is gone, a man is fortunate if he bows to the inevitable with the grace, wit and green memories of Victor Hugo, a formidable boudoir athlete in his time.

Hugo was accorded the rare distinction of an invitation to receive the acclaim of the French Senate when he was eighty-two. "Gentlemen of France," he began, "it is difficult for a man of my years to address such an august body. Almost as difficult as it is for a man of my years to make love three—no, four—times in one afternoon to a woman."

# 12

# A Mutual Seduction

✳ ✳ ✳

A MIDDLE-AGED MAN DISTURBED BY HIS FALTERING SEX DRIVE
and straining to step it up always gropes for the wrong remedy
for the wrong malady. His problem is not the inability to make
love, but an incapacity to give love, and new bedmates with
booster shots of erotic excitement will not resolve his dilemma. Professional counselors can suggest the answer, but
he must find it within himself. To paraphrase Clemenceau's
dictum on war, sex is far too serious a matter to be left to
psychiatrists.

The limitations of the fifty-minute crutch are freely con-
ceded by Dr. Theodor Reik: "Although psychoanalysis has
the unclaimed merit of removing many sexual inhibitions and
suppressions, it has failed to deal with the problem of affection.
Even after analysis, many men and women are unable to love,
to give and receive tenderness. Many patients who come to
psychoanalysis with emotional problems which were often
connected with their sex life were freed from inhibitions and
achieved normal attitudes toward sex. Many of them reached a
purely mechanical sexual release in promiscuous relationships.
Before undertaking psychoanalysis they were, perhaps, afraid
of going to the dogs. After their sexual inhibitions were removed, quite a few of them might well have been afraid that
they had indeed arrived there."

People who are disappointed in love rail at their bad luck
with incompatible partners, but their failure is self-made and
self-perpetuating. Marriage is governed by so many chance

events—where you live, the friends you make, where you happened to be at a particular time and place—that random factors must be discounted. Well-mated couples have no greater control over the same accidental circumstances.

Somewhere, perhaps on the next street, there undoubtedly was a girl better suited temperamentally for every man than the wife he chose. Had he met and married her, he might have had a different number of children; he might be living elsewhere; he might have made business and social contacts that influenced his career, for better or worse. But the quality of his love life would be substantially the same—barring marriage to a confirmed neurotic—for the essential elements of a mature sexual relationship do not change with one woman to the next.

Good marriages are not made in heaven. Love is an art and, like everything worth achieving, it requires effort, knowledge and singleness of purpose. Everyone wants to be loved, but love is not a passive emotion. It must be given to be received. It is not a popularity contest in which prizes are awarded to the most successful men or the most attractive women. The good provider who expends more energy and attention on the acquisition of money and status than to the cultivation of love may command the gratitude of his wife and children, but he does not forge an abiding bond with them. A beautiful woman wrapped up in "her adored self" is desired by many men and loved by none if she does not return an equal measure of the affection she receives.

Love is a mutual seduction. A man and a woman want one another, because in sexual fusion they find spiritual union. Each is incomplete without the other. This need, this hunger, for psychic totality is constant, and it is, therefore, a more powerful aphrodisiac than a libidinous fillip that arouses desire for a fleeting moment, then seems coarse and banal after the physical impulse has been satisfied.

Those who are incapable of love decry the personal sacrifices it entails. People in love speak of sharing their personal happiness as well as burdens. Sharing breaks down the barriers of separateness and relieves the desolate feeling of isolation that is the source of all anxiety. A couple who enjoy the rewards of sex, the most reciprocal of all human relationships, is better fortified to withstand the stresses of life. It is the core of their confidence and common interests.

The sustaining power of love was summed up eloquently by Bertrand Russell in the opening paragraphs of his autobiography: "Three passions, simple but overwhelmingly strong, have governed my life: the longing for love, the search for knowledge, and unbearable pity for the suffering of mankind. These passions, like great winds, have blown me hither and thither, in a wayward course, over a deep ocean of anguish, reaching to the very verge of despair.

"I have sought love, first, because it brings ecstasy—ecstasy so great that I would often have sacrificed all the rest of life for a few hours of this joy. I have sought it, next, because it relieves loneliness—that terrible loneliness in which one shivering consciousness looks over the rim of the world into the cold unfathomable lifeless abyss. I have sought it, finally, because in the union of love I have seen, in a mystic miniature, the prefiguring vision of the heaven that saints and poets have imagined. This is what I sought, and though it might seem too good for human life, this is what—at last—I have found."

Love is concentrated on a special, specific man or woman. The crude sex drive is impersonal; it can be appeased without exchanging a word with a stranger or, for that matter, alone in masturbation. Since crude sex is directed to genital sensation rather than to emotional unity it is safe, uncomplicated pleasure without responsibility, but it is a blind alley. The sense of isolation is intensified when, after the pleasure has passed, casual partners separate and each is alone and unfulfilled. There is no escape from it in alcohol, drugs or even familiar partners. A man is never more alone than when he is locked in a loveless sexual embrace.

The age-old sexual anxieties of men, which are aroused today earlier than ever before by the fear of financial insecurity, have been compounded by the leering emphasis on cheap, quick thrills. Eroticism is a wholesome and vibrant ingredient of sexuality when its purpose is to promote pleasure in foreplay and heighten anticipation of intercourse. But in the turned-on, hooked-in subculture of youth, which the middle-aged have permitted to run roughshod over them, the scavenging for sensations of the moment is counterfeit sex that debases physical love.

Philosophers as well as fools were falling into the trap of idolizing youth long before it was an economic asset. "Youth without beauty has still always attractions; beauty without youth has none," Schopenhauer wrote. The nonsensical idea that sex is only for the young, the staple theme of movies, television and popular fiction, has led too many middle-aged men and women to the greater nonsense of imitating youth's restless search for new, transitory experiences rather than one deep emotional attachment. That is how it should be—for the young and inquisitive.

A mature attitude toward sex is centered on a durable relationship with one person. From the hedonists to the hippies, promiscuity has been defended on the grounds that man is not a monogamous animal, a thoroughly specious argument biologically and historically. As we have seen, every advanced culture that sanctioned polygamy eventually abandoned it. Experience taught men that sex is most gratifying when it is a coefficient of love, and love cannot be shared with more than one woman.

It is a lesson every man learns, sometimes at an exorbitant cost. Relatively few husbands probably are absolutely faithful throughout marriage, but the more pertinent fact is that the overwhelming majority stop making passes at targets of opportunity by the time they reach middle age. Morality, qualms of conscience or loss of speed afoot does not impel them to retire from the chase. They finally realize that intercourse is better with the wives they love than it is likely to be with other women, despite the excitement of illicit sex.

Once a man has known love—or thought he has—and loses it, he seldom plays the field, inviting as the prospect appears. Fully 70 percent of the men who are divorced after forty-five quickly remarry to establish a permanent relationship with one woman—the only condition under which physical love can flourish.

"Love gives to every power a double power," Shakespeare said. It may be corny to harp on love as the requisite for sexual fulfillment, but a sentiment must have kernels of enduring truth to become hackneyed. It is a natural law that two inanimate objects have a mutual attraction. A man and a woman are born with a need for each other that will draw them together irresistibly if they give themselves half a chance to let nature take its course.

# Bibliography

Ackerman, Nathan. *The Psychodynamics of Family Life.* Basic Books, Inc.

Allen, Frederick L. *Only Yesterday.* Harper & Row.

Arabanel, Albert (editor). *The Encyclopedia of Sexual Behavior.* Hawthorn Books.

Argyris, Chris. "The Organization: What Makes It Healthy?" *Harvard Business Review,* November, 1958.

Arieti, Silvano (editor). *American Handbook of Psychiatry.* Basic Books, Inc.

Artiss, Kenneth L. "Human Behavior Under Stress—From Combat to Social Psychiatry." *Military Medicine.* October, 1963.

Bacon, Selden. "The Alcoholic Executive." *Fortune.* January, 1960.

Barron, Milton. *The Aging American.* T.Y. Crowell Co.

Beach, Frank, and Ford, Clellan. *Patterns of Sexual Behavior.* Harper & Row.

Bell, Daniel. *Work and Its Discontents.* Beacon Press.

Belton, C.H. "The Sex Factor in Marriage and Its Significance in Neurosis and Divorce." *New Zealand Medical Journal.* May, 1961.

Benedek, Therese. *Psychosexual Functions in Women.* Ronald Press.

Benedict, Ruth. *Patterns of Culture.* Penguin Books.

Benjamin, Harry. "Impotence and Aging." *Sexology.* November, 1959.

———. "The Sex Problem in the Armed Forces." *Urologic and Cutaneous Review.* May, 1944.

Bergler, Edmund. *The Revolt of the Middle-Aged Man.* Grosset and Dunlap.

———. *Counterfeit Sex.* Grove Press.

Binder, Pearl. *The Peacock's Tail.* Harrap.

Birren, James E. *Handbook of Aging and the Individual.* University of Chicago Press.

Blanton, Smiley. *Now or Never.* Prentice-Hall.

Boehm, George. "The Search for Ways to Keep Youthful." *Fortune.* March, 1965.

Bonaparte, Marie. *Female Sexuality.* Grove Press.

Bowman, Karl. "The Sex Life of the Aging Individual." *Geriatrics.* February, 1954.

Braceland, Francis. "Men in Their Fifties." *Journal of the Omaha Mid-West Clinical Society.* January, 1954.

Bradburn, Norman. *In Pursuit of Happiness.* University of Chicago Press.

Brayshaw, A. Joseph. "Middle-Aged Marriage." *Marriage and Family Living.* November, 1962.

Briffault, Robert. *The Mother.* The Macmillan Company.

Brill, A.A. *Lectures on Psychoanalytic Psychiatry.* Alfred A. Knopf, Inc.

Brill, Norman, and Beebe, Gilbert. *A Follow-Up Study of War Neurosis.* National Research Council.

Browning, William. "The Climacteric and Impotence." *International Record of Medicine.* November, 1960.

Canby, H.S., "Sex and Marriage in the Nineties." *Harper's.* September, 1934.

Christenson, Cornelia, and Gagnon, John. "Sexual Behavior in a Group of Older Women." *Journal of Gerontology.* July, 1965.

Claman, A.D. (chairman, panel discussion). "Sexual Difficulties After Fifty." *The Canadian Medical Association Journal.* January 29, 1966.

Clark, Alexander L., and Wallin, Paul. "Women's Sexual Responsiveness and the Duration and Quality of Their Marriages." *American Journal of Sociology.* September, 1965.

Clark, LeMon. "Sex Life of the Middle Aged." *Marriage and Family Living.* April, 1949.

Comfort, Alexander. *Sexual Behavior in Society.* Gerald Duckworth and Co.

Cowdry, E.V. *Problems of Aging.* Williams and Wilkins Co.

Davis, Katherine. *Factors in the Sex Life of Twenty-Two Hundred Women.* Harper & Row.

Davis, Maxine. *The Sexual Responsibility of Woman.* Dial Press.

Dawkins, Sylvia. "Non-Consummation of Marriage." *Lancet.* November 4, 1961.

Dell, Floyd. *Love in the Machine Age.* Farrar and Rinehart.

DeRopp, Robert. *Man Against Aging.* St. Martin's Press.

Deutsch, Albert (editor). *Sex Habits of American Men.* Prentice-Hall.

Deutsch, Helene. *The Psychology of Women.* Grune and Stratton.

Dickinson, Robert L. *Human Sex Anatomy.* Williams and Wilkins Co.

Douglas, Robert. "The Male Climacteric." *Journal of Urology.* March, 1941.

Dublin, Louis, and Spiegelman, M. *The Facts of Life, From Birth to Death.* The Macmillan Company.

Duhl, Leonard. "The American Character—Crisis, Change and Complexity." *Journal of Nervous and Mental Disease.* August, 1963.

Durant, Will. *The Story of Philosophy.* Simon and Schuster.

Duvall, S.M. *Women and Morals*. Association Press.

Ellis, Albert. *The Art and Science of Love*. Lyle Stuart.

Ellis, Havelock. *Studies in the Psychology of Sex*. F.A. Davis Co.

English, O. Spurgeon, and Pearson, Gerald. *Emotional Problems of Living*. W.W. Norton Co.

Farnsworth, Dana L. "Health Under Pressure." *Harvard Business Review*. November, 1957.

Finkle, Alexander L. "Sex Problems in Later Years." *Medical Times*. April, 1967.

———. "Sexual Potency in Aging Males." *Journal of the American Medical Association*. July 18, 1959.

Firth, Raymond. *Human Types*. T. Nelson and Sons.

*Fortune* editors. *The Executive Life*. Doubleday and Co.

Freegood, Seymour. "Life in Bloomfield Hills." *Fortune*. July, 1961.

Freeman, Joseph. "Sexual Capacities in the Aging Male." *Geriatrics*. January, 1961.

Freud, Sigmund. *The Basic Writings of Sigmund Freud*. Modern Library.

———. *Collected Papers*. The Hogarth Press.

———. *Sexuality and the Psychology of Love*. Collier Books.

———. *A General Introduction to Psychoanalysis*. Doubleday and Co.

Fried, Edrita. *On Love and Sexuality*. Grove Press.

Fromm, Erich. *The Art of Loving*. Harper and Row.

Gantt, W. Horsley. *Disturbances in Sexual Functions During Stress*. Association for Research in Nervous and Mental Diseases.

Gardner, L. Pearl. "Attitudes and Activities of the Middle-Aged and Aged." *Geriatrics*. January, 1949.

Geddes, Donald P. (editor). *An Analysis of the Kinsey Reports*. New American Library.

Gens, Ruth. "Male Hypersexual Behavior." *Journal of the American Medical Women's Association*. March, 1964.

Gitelson, Maxwell. "The Emotional Problems of Elderly People." *Geriatrics*. May, 1948.

Gordon, Richard, and Gunther, Max. *The Split-Level Trap*. Dell Books.

Gorer, Geoffrey. *The Marquis de Sade*. Liveright Publishing Corp.

Graves, Robert. *The Greek Myths*. Penguin Books.

Gray, Madeline. *The Changing Years*. Doubleday and Co.

Grinker, Roy, and Spiegel, John. *Men Under Stress*. Blakiston.

Gross, Nancy. *Living with Stress*. McGraw-Hill.

Halliday, James. "Epidemiology and the Psychosomatic Affections." *Lancet*. August 10, 1946.

Hamilton, G. V., and MacGowan, K. *What Is Wrong with Marriage*. A. and C. Boni.

Hediger, H. *Wild Animals in Captivity*. Butterworth.

Heyder, D.W., and Wambach, Helen. "Sexuality and Effect on Frogmen." *Archives of General Psychiatry*. September, 1964.

Hirsch, Edwin. *The Power to Love*. Pyramid Books.

Hotchkiss, R.S. *Fertility in Men*. J.B. Lippincott Co.

Jacobson, Paul. *American Marriage and Divorce*. Rinehart.

Jenkins, Ray. *Victorian Scandal*. Chilmark Press.

Jones, Ernest. *The Life and Work of Sigmund Freud*. Basic Books, Inc.

Kaplan, Oscar (editor). *Mental Disorders in Later Life*. Stanford University Press.

Kardiner, Abram. *Sex and Morality*. Bobbs-Merrill Co.

————. *War Stress and Neurotic Illness*. P.B. Hoeber.

Kaufman, Joseph, and Borgeson, Griffith. *Man and Sex*. Simon and Schuster.

Kenyon, Herbert. *The Prostate Gland*. Random House.

Kinsey, Alfred, *et al*. *Sexual Behavior in the Human Male*. W.B. Saunders Co.

————. *Sexual Behavior in the Human Female*. W.B. Saunders Co.

Kleegman, Sophia. "Attitudes of Frigid Women." *Quarterly Review of Surgery, Obstetrics and Gynecology*. October, 1959.

Kluckhohn, Clyde. *Culture and Behavior*. Glencoe.

Krafft-Ebing, Richard. *Aberrations of Sexual Life*. Staples Press.

Krich, A.M. (editor). *Men*. Dell Books.

————. (editor). *The Anatomy of Love*. Dell Books.

Landis, Judson T., and Mary G. *Building a Successful Marriage*. Prentice-Hall.

Leuba, Clarence. *The Sexual Nature of Man*. Doubleday and Co.

Levin, Sidney. "Some Comments on the Distribution of Narcissistic and Object Libido of the Aged." *Internal Journal of Psychoanalysis*. April, 1965.

Lewin, S.A., and Gilmore, J. *Sex after Forty*. Medical Research Press.

London, Louis. "What Is the Libido?" *Medical Times*. March, 1961.

Lowie, Robert. *Primitive Society*. Harper & Row.

Mantegazza, Paolo. *The Physiology of Love*. Eugenics Publishing Co.

Marshall, S.L.A. "Men Against Fire." *Infantry Journal*.

Masters, William H., and Johnson, Virginia. *Human Sexual Response*. Little, Brown and Co.

Mead, Margaret. *Male and Female*. William Morrow and Co.

Menninger, Karl. *Man Against Himself*. Harcourt, Brace and World.

Meyers, George, and Heller, Carl. "The Male Climacteric." *Journal of the American Medical Association*. October 21, 1944.

Meyers, Thomas J. "The Clitorid Woman." *The Psychiatric Quarterly*. April, 1966.

Montagu, Ashley. *The Natural Superiority of Women*. The Macmillan Company.

Mumford, Lewis. *The Condition of Man*. Harcourt, Brace and World.
———. *The Culture of Cities*. Harcourt, Brace and World.
Murdock, George. *Social Structure*. The Macmillan Company.
Newman, Gustave, and Nichols, Claude. "Sexual Activities and Attitudes in Older Persons." *Journal of the American Medical Association*. May 7, 1960.
Packard, Vance. *The Pyramid Climbers*. McGraw-Hill Co.
*Psychiatric Experiences of the Eighth Air Force*. Army Air Forces.
Rainier, Jerome, and Julia. *Sexual Pleasure in Marriage*. Pocket Books, Inc.
Reik, Theodor. *Psychology of Sex Relations*. Rinehart and Co.
———. *Sex in Man and Woman*. Noonday Press.
Rennie, *et al*. "Urban Life and Mental Health." *American Journal of Psychiatry*. March, 1957.
Robinson, Marie. *The Power of Sexual Surrender*. Doubleday and Co.
Roen, Philip. "Impotence: A Concise Review." *New York State Journal of Medicine*. October 15, 1965.
Rubin, Alan, and Babbott, David. "Impotence and Diabetes Mellitus." *Journal of the American Medical Association*. October 4, 1958.
Rubin, Isador. *Sexual Life after Sixty*. Basic Books, Inc.
———. "Mental Sex Behavior." *Medical Times*. March, 1964.
Russek, Henry. "Emotional Stress and Coronary Heart Disease in American Physicians, Dentists and Lawyers." *American Journal of the Medical Sciences*. June, 1962.
Russell, Bertrand. *The Autobiography of Bertrand Russell*. Little, Brown and Co.
Ryan, Thomas A. *Work and Effort*. Ronald Press.
Sapirstein, Milton. *Paradoxes of Everyday Life*. Fawcett Publications, Inc.
Saunders, Dero. "Executive Discontent." *Fortune*. October, 1956.
Schapiro, Bernard. "Premature Ejaculation." *Journal of Urology*. September, 1943.
Scheinfeld, Aram. *Men and Women*. Harcourt, Brace and World.
Schwarz, Oswald. *The Psychology of Sex*. Penguin Books.
Segal, Morey. "Impulsive Sexuality." *International Journal of Psychoanalysis*. October, 1963.
Selye, Hans. *The Stress of Life*. New York Academy of Medicine.
Seward, Georgene. *Sex and the Social Order*. McGraw-Hill Co.
Sherfey, Mary Jane. "The Evolution and Nature of Female Sexuality." *Journal of the American Psychoanalytic Association*. January, 1966.
Simon, Alexander. "Psychological Problems of the Aging." *California Medicine*. August, 1951.
Smith, Ethel. *The Dynamics of Aging*. W.W. Norton.
Smith, Richard A. "The Executive Crack-Up." *Fortune*. May, 1955.
Sorokin, P.A. *The Crisis of Our Age*. E.P. Dutton and Co.
Spectorsky, A.C. *The Exurbanites*. Berkley Publishing Co.

Stein, Joseph. *Maturity in Sex and Marriage.* Coward-McCann, Inc.

Stekel, Wilhelm. *Impotence in the Male.* Boni and Liveright, Inc.

──────. *Twelve Essays on Sex and Psychoanalysis.* Eugenic Publishing Co.

Stokes, Walter R. "Sexual Function in the Aging Male." *Geriatrics.* September, 1951.

Stone, Abraham and Hannah. *A Marriage Manual.* Simon and Schuster.

Stopes, Marie. *Married Love.* Eugenics Publishing Co.

Super, Donald. *The Psychology of Careers.* Harper & Row.

Terman, Louis and Miles, C.C. *Sex and Personality.* McGraw-Hill Co.

──────. *Psychological Factors in Marital Happiness.* McGraw-Hill Co.

Van de Velde, Theodore. *Ideal Marriage.* Random House, Inc.

Vatsyayana. *The Kama Sutra.* Society for the Friends of India.

Walker, Kenneth, and Fletcher, Peter. *Sex and Society.* Oxford University Press.

Wallin, Paul. "A Study of Orgasm as a Condition of Women's Enjoyment of Intercourse." *Journal of Social Psychology.* February, 1960.

Wallin, Paul, and Clark, Alexander. "Marital Satisfaction." *Journal of Abnormal and Social Psychology.* November, 1958.

Werner, August A. "The Male Climacteric." *Journal of the American Medical Association.* April 15, 1939.

──────. "The Male Climacteric." *Journal of Urology.* June, 1943.

──────. "The Male Climacteric." *Journal of the American Medical Association.* March 24, 1945.

Wesson, Miley. "The Value of Testosterone to Men Past Middle Age." *Journal of the American Geriatrics Society.* December, 1964.

Whyte, William H. *The Organization Man.* Simon and Schuster.

Wile, Ira. *The Sex Life of the Unmarried Adult.* Vanguard Press.

# INDEX

# INDEX